**EFFECTIVE TEACHING
AND LEARNING**

Numeracy

RESEARCH TEAM

Principal investigators

Diana Coben, Margaret Brown

Researchers

Valerie Rhodes, Jon Swain, Katerina Ananiadou

Researcher and administrative support

Peter Brown

Teacher researchers

Jackie Ashton, Debbie Holder, Sandra Lowe, Cathy Magee,

Sue Nieduszynska, Veronica Storey

SERIES EDITOR

John Vorhaus

CONTENTS

Acknowledgements

The authors would like to thank all the teachers and learners who participated in this project.

Peer review
This report was peer reviewed. The critical reviewers from research and practice were:

Gail Fitzsimons, Monash University, Australia
Katherine Safford, St Peter's College, USA
Jan Tetley, Wakefield College
Malcolm Swan, University of Nottingham
Pat Dreyer, CEP Associates
Cathy France, Thomas Danby College
Terry Maguire, University of Limerick
Oonagh Gormley, NRDC, Institute of Education, University of London
Dave Baker, Institute of Education, University of London

Preface

The *Skills for Life* Strategy in England has led to unprecedented investment in adult literacy, language and numeracy (LLN), major reforms of teacher education and training, and the introduction of national standards, core curricula and assessment to inform teaching and learning. We have a unique opportunity to make a step change in improving levels of adult skills. But until recently too little was known about effective teaching and learning practices, and reports from Ofsted and the Adult Learning Inspectorate repeatedly drew attention to the quality of teaching, and the need for standards to improve.

It has been a strategic priority at the National Research and Development Centre for Adult Literacy and Numeracy (NRDC) to investigate teaching and learning practices in all the subject areas and settings in *Skills for Life*, to report on the most promising and effective practices, and to provide teachers and trainers, along with policy-makers and researchers, with an unparalleled evidence base on which to build on the progress already made.

Our findings and recommendations are reported here, and in the four companion reports covering reading, writing, ESOL and ICT. The five studies, which have been co-ordinated by NRDC Associate Director John Vorhaus, provide material for improving the quality of teaching and learning, and for informing developments in initial teacher education and continuing professional development (CPD). We are also preparing a range of practitioner guides and development materials, as a major new resource for teachers and teacher educators. They will explore and develop the examples of good and promising practice documented in these pages.

Until recently adult numeracy was under-researched and underdeveloped, and it was often not distinguished from literacy in policy documents and inspection reports. However, the profile of numeracy has been steadily rising, following confirmation by national and international surveys of low levels of skill amongst the adult population. This study is the largest undertaken into adult numeracy in the UK, and it represents a substantial advance in our understanding of the practices that contribute to successful teaching and learning.

Ursula Howard, Director, NRDC

1 Executive summary

1.1 The Effective Practice Studies

The five NRDC Effective Practice Studies explore teaching and learning in reading, writing, numeracy, ESOL and ICT, and they set out to answer two questions:

1. How can teaching, learning and assessing literacy, numeracy, ESOL and ICT be improved?
2. Which factors contribute to successful learning?

Even before NRDC was set up it was apparent from reviews of the field (Brooks et al., 2001; Kruidenier, 2002) that there was little reliable research-based evidence to answer these questions. Various NRDC reviews showed that progress in amassing such evidence, though welcome where it was occurring, was slow (Coben et al., 2003; Barton and Pitt, 2003; Torgerson et al., 2003, 2004, 2005). Four preliminary studies on reading, writing, ESOL and ICT, were undertaken between 2002 and 2004 (Besser et al., 2004; Kelly et al., 2004; Roberts et al., 2004; Mellar et al., 2004). However, we recognised the urgent need to build on these in order greatly to increase the research base for the practice of teaching these subjects.

The inspiration for the design of the five projects was a study in the US of the teaching of literacy and English language to adult learners for whom English is an additional language (Condelli et al., 2003). This study was the first of its kind, and the lead author, Larry Condelli of the American Institutes for Research, has acted as an expert adviser on all five NRDC projects.

The research began in July 2003 and was completed in March 2006. It set out to recruit and gather information on 500 learners in each study, assess their attainment and attitudes at two points during the year in which they were participating in the study, interview both learners and teachers, observe the strategies the teachers used, and correlate those strategies with changes in the learners' attainment and attitudes.

The ICT study differed from the others in that its first phase was developmental, its sample size was smaller, and it had a shorter timescale, completing in March 2005.

1.2 The numeracy study

We investigated approaches to the teaching of numeracy, aiming to identify the extent of learners' progress, and to establish correlations between this progress and the strategies and practices used by teachers.

The study involved 412 learners and 34 teachers in 47 classes. Two-thirds of the classes were in further education (FE) colleges. The average teaching session was just under two hours and average attendance in class was eight learners.

In total, 250 learners were assessed and 243 completed attitude surveys. Classes were observed between one and four times during each course. Background information was collected on teachers and learners, and we carried out interviews with 33 teachers and 112 learners.

1.3 Main findings

Progress

We found evidence of significant progress, with an average gain of 9 per cent in test scores, although there was a wide range of average gains between different classes.

Learners' attitudes were more positive at the end of the course, with the changes tending to be greatest for older people.

Once learners overcome initial anxiety about the course and about mathematics, numeracy courses can have a significant and positive effect on their identities. They can improve confidence and self-esteem, and enable learners to develop new aspirations and form new dispositions towards learning.

For some learners, to maintain their level of skills, knowledge and understanding is a sign of personal progress.

Time to learn

Evidence from the National Center for the Study of Adult Learning and Literacy (NCSALL) in the US suggests that learners require between 150 and 200 hours of study if they are to progress by one level within the *Skills for Life* qualification framework. However, although average attendance by learners between our first and second assessments was only 39 hours, we found that many had made significant progress. Others needed longer to consolidate their learning.

Teaching strategies

Teachers valued 'flexibility' as a key feature of effective practice. The diversity of learners, contexts and session lengths meant that no one pattern of lesson activity appeared to be optimal.

A wide range of different teaching approaches was observed, although whole class and individual work predominated.

Most teachers gave clear explanations, which were much valued by learners. They also broke work down into smaller steps and gave feedback to learners about their work.

Most teachers followed a set scheme of work, and few incorporated learners' personal interests. It was also less usual for teachers to differentiate work, make connections to other areas of mathematics, or ask higher-order questions to encourage higher-level thinking or probe learners' misconceptions.

Although activities were often varied, there was little use of practical resources or ICT, little group or collaborative work, and it was unusual to find learners collaborating with, and learning from, each other.

Teaching and learning relationships

Over 90 per cent of learners interviewed expressed a high level of satisfaction with their course and their teacher. Learners were usually highly engaged. They were often but not always challenged and stretched, were given time to gain understanding, and the majority had their individual needs met.

Learners recognised that the relationship between the teacher and effective learning was critical. It was important for teachers to develop good relationships with learners and to treat, and respect, them as adults. Classroom observation indicated that teachers were enthusiastic, generous in giving praise, and there was a high level of mutual respect.

Teachers' qualifications

The teachers were generally experienced and well-qualified, with many having previously taught mathematics in primary and/or secondary schools. Teachers' subject knowledge was generally adequate.

Twenty-seven (79 per cent) of the 34 teachers reported having a formal qualification in mathematics or a related subject (e.g. science). Thirty teachers (88 per cent) reported having a teaching qualification. Six (18 per cent) of the teachers reported having a subject-specific Level 4 qualification for teaching numeracy to adults.

It is often assumed that individuals holding high qualifications in mathematics are able to teach basic concepts at lower levels of mathematics. We did not always find evidence of this. Some teachers relied on methods they had been taught at school.

1.4 Recommendations

Development work and quality improvement

In the Subject Specifications for Adult Numeracy, and in generic courses (e.g. Cert Ed. or PGCE), there should be a requirement for teachers to have a firm understanding of basic concepts: place-value, multiplication and division, for example.

Teachers need a firm grasp of subject and pedagogical knowledge, and also subject-specific pedagogic knowledge. This enables them to be flexible in their approaches, and to cater to the diversity of learners and provision in adult numeracy.

Policy

Adult numeracy education should be seen as part of mathematics education, and as a discrete subject in relation to adult literacy and other *Skills for Life* areas. This should be reflected in policy documents and in the organisation and inspection of provision, so that, for example, adult numeracy provision is effectively co-ordinated with other mathematics provision offered by colleges and other organisations.

Research

Further research and development should be undertaken into learner assessment in numeracy at *Skills for Life* levels with a view to developing an appropriate assessment instrument for research purposes. More sensitivity would be achieved if an instrument were designed to focus on a narrow range of initial attainment: Entry levels 1 and 2, for example.

A bank of secure, reliable and valid questions should be available to match assessment questions to individual teaching programmes, and therefore to provide a more genuine test of learning in relation to teaching.

More research is required to explore learner and teacher identities. Learners' identities affect attitudes, motivations, dispositions towards mathematics and education in general, relations with peers and teachers, and future expectations and aspirations. Teacher identities also matter: we need to know how much personal investment teachers make both as numeracy teachers and as mathematicians.

1.5 Limitations to this research

We acknowledge the following limitations to our research.

The heterogeneous nature of adult numeracy teaching, the range of learners and the number of variables amongst teachers and learners, make it difficult to identify effective practices and factors that can be generalised with confidence across the whole sector.

There were problems finding an assessment instrument that was both short and appropriate to sensitively and validly measure progress across such a diverse learner group. There were particular difficulties for adults with lower ability levels, and with reading or language difficulties (two in every five learners in the sample spoke English as an additional language).

The areas of mathematics taught in class may not have matched those covered in the assessment we used. We therefore cannot be certain that newly correct answers in the second assessment resulted from class teaching rather than other sources of learning.

The need for the assessment instrument to be practicable – not take up too much class time – meant that there was an inevitable trade-off between getting more information and taking up too much of the learners' time in class.

The short teaching time of only 39 hours between first and second assessments is likely to have been too short to show evidence of more substantial progress.

Some courses were designed on a roll-on/roll-off basis which meant that some learners who had taken the first test were no longer there at the second. Equally, new learners may have arrived who had not taken the first assessment and were therefore ineligible for the second. About 40 per cent of learners left their course for a variety of reasons, and the effect of this was compounded when researchers came to administer the second assessment if the class was poorly attended on that particular day.

Factors which cannot easily be determined in a large-scale survey may have had more influence on their learning than any specific, easily observed difference in teacher behaviour. These are: learners' strength of motivation, their persistence, their aspirations, their abilities and dispositions towards numeracy, how they position themselves as learners in relation to the subject matter, the teacher and other learners, and their socio-cultural background and previous experiences, both inside and outside the classroom.

2 Context

This chapter sets the study within the current national policy context, and as part of the research agenda developed by the NRDC. It states the research aims, and provides information on the sample, methods and ethical considerations.

2.1 The policy background

Until comparatively recently, adult numeracy has been under-researched and under-developed. However, the low levels of numeracy skill among adults, as revealed by national and international surveys, have begun to make numeracy an important area for research. The study is set within the context of the Government's *Skills for Life* Strategy to improve adult literacy and numeracy in England (DfEE, 2001), and took place against a backdrop of policy changes in adult numeracy education (DfEE, 1999, 2001; QCA, 2000; DfES, 2001; DfES/FENTO, 2002), post-14 mathematics education and training (Smith, 2004; Tomlinson, 2004; DfES, 2005a), initial teacher education (ITE) (DfES/FENTO, 2002) and concerns about levels of skill in the adult population (DfES/DWP/HMT 2005). The recent interim review by Lord Leitch for HM Treasury, *Skills in the UK: The long term challenge*, calls for the UK to 'become world class on skills – for all of our sakes' (Leitch, 2005: 2). Numeracy is key to achieving that aim and, as the title of a recent review of evidence from the British Birth Cohort Studies shows, *Numeracy Matters More* to individuals and society (Parsons and Bynner, 2005).

In *Skills for Life*, literacy and numeracy are promoted as basic skills to be acquired and utilised by adults in the workplace and elsewhere. Numeracy is defined as the ability 'to use mathematics at a level necessary to function at work and in society in general' (DfEE, 1999). The *Skills for Life* target is for 1.5 million adults to improve their literacy and numeracy skills by 2007 (DfES 2003a). This target should be seen against the background of the extent of need for literacy and numeracy in the adult population. The *Skills for Life Survey* commissioned by the Department for Education and Skills (DfES) found that nearly half of all adults of working age in England (47 per cent; 15 million adults) were classified at or below the level expected of an average 11-year-old in numeracy (DfES, 2003a: 19).

At the same time, a disturbing picture of adult numeracy education began to emerge, with a shortage of experienced teachers and teacher trainers. For example, a report by the Inspectorate in 2003 found that numeracy is taught less frequently than literacy, and there is less demand for numeracy despite equivalent levels of need (in fact, greater need, according to the *Skills for Life Survey*). The report also found there is a need for greater expertise in teaching numeracy, and numeracy is too often taught by rote rather than by understanding numerical concepts (ALI/OFSTED, 2003). The Smith Report acknowledges that the adult numeracy strategy is challenging and demanding for teachers and learners alike (Smith, 2004). Work is currently under way on implementing the Smith recommendations, including measures designed to raise the profile of mathematics, improve the supply of teachers and support CPD, while reviewing the curriculum, assessment and qualifications frameworks.

What counts as effective practice in adult numeracy education in this context is both complex and straightforward. It is straightforward insofar as adult numeracy provision is inspected according to standards set out in the Common Inspection Framework (ALI/OFSTED, 2001) by the Office for Standards in Education (OFSTED) and the Adult Learning Inspectorate (ALI)[1]. However, little is known about effective practice in adult numeracy education from a research perspective and the tendency has been for numeracy to be overshadowed by literacy in official reports, including Inspection reports, so that information about adult numeracy is often impossible to untangle from that on adult literacy. The relationship between effective teaching and successful learning in adult numeracy has yet to be established; this study represents a step towards this goal.

2.2 The Effective Practice Studies

The project reported here was conducted as part of the research agenda developed by the NRDC, which is part of the *Skills for Life* Strategy (DfEE, 2001) of the DfES in England.

The project was one of a suite of four which had the common aim of investigating effective teaching of literacy, language and numeracy to adults. The skills which the four projects covered, and the organisations which conducted them, were:

Reading	University of Sheffield
Writing	Learning and Skills Development Agency
English for speakers of other languages (ESOL)	University of Leeds and King's College London
Numeracy	King's College London.

A fifth project covered ICT; this was conducted by the Institute of Education, University of London. It differed in that its first phase was developmental, rather than evaluative; as a consequence, only the second phase of its data-gathering resembled that of the other four projects, and its final sample size was smaller. Also, it had a shorter timescale, being completed in March 2005.

The other four projects all began in July 2003 and were completed in March 2006. The motives for them were the questions posed in NRDC's Strategy, published in July 2003 (NRDC, 2003:30):

- How can teaching, learning and assessing literacy, numeracy and ESOL be improved?
- What factors contribute to successful learning?

Even before the NRDC was set up it was apparent from reviews of the field (Brooks et al., 2001; Kruidenier, 2002) that little reliable research-based evidence existed to answer these questions, and various NRDC reviews showed that progress in amassing such evidence, though welcome where it was occurring, was slow (Coben et al., 2003; Barton and Pitt, 2003; Torgerson et al., 2003, 2004, 2005). Four preliminary studies, on reading, writing, ESOL and ICT, were undertaken between 2002 and 2004 (Besser et al., 2004; Kelly et al., 2004; Roberts et al., 2004; Mellar et al., 2004, respectively). However, NRDC recognised a need to build on these to expand the research base on the practice of teaching these subjects and therefore

---

1 The Government has recently announced that a new single organisation is to be created by merging the activities of OFSTED with the children's social care remit of the Commission for Social Care Inspection (CSCI), the Children and Family Court Advisory and Support Service (CAFCASS) inspection remit of HM Inspectorate of Court Administration (HMICA) and the Adult Learning Inspectorate (ALI) (http://www.ali.gov.uk/News/Talisman/issue_48/Strategy+board+appointed.htm, accessed 17 Feb. 2006).

the information available to policy-makers and professionals, both teachers and trainers.

The inspiration for the design of the reading, writing, ESOL and numeracy projects, and the second year of the ICT project, was a US study of the teaching of literacy and English language to adult learners for whom English is an additional language (Condelli et al., 2003).

The projects were in two phases, in academic years 2003/04 and 2004/05. The targets across the two years were to recruit and gather background data on about 250 learners, assess their attainment and attitudes at two points during the year in which they were in the study, interview both learners and teachers, observe the strategies their teachers used, and correlate those strategies with changes in the learners' attainment and attitudes.

2.3 Sample and methods

The numeracy research project team consisted of the project directors, professional researchers, and six trained teacher-researchers.

Adult numeracy tuition is diverse in its range of provision, settings, teachers and the different purposes of learners; it is offered both as a discrete subject and 'embedded' in other subjects and vocational areas. Its purposes include academic and recreational study, vocational training, basic skills and workforce development and the enhancement of parents' involvement with children and schools. Learning contexts include further education (FE), work-based learning, Jobcentre Plus, Ufl learndirect, adult and community education (ACE), family numeracy and prisons. Courses vary in length, with a variety of accreditation and qualifications, and may have titles that do not emphasise their numeracy content, making it difficult to track down relevant provision. There is a wide range of learners of different ages, with various experiences of schooling and a variety of motivations, dispositions, aspirations and needs, including more non-traditional adult learners and 16 to 19-year-olds. Reliable data on the adult numeracy teaching workforce are unavailable, but it is likely that such teachers vary in their experience of teaching adults in different contexts, their knowledge of mathematics and numeracy/mathematics pedagogy (issues around teachers' subject-specific pedagogy are discussed in Chapter 9), and their teaching qualifications. Many teach part-time and have originally taught in other curriculum areas such as literacy and ESOL. We aimed to reflect the diversity of numeracy provision, and the range of adult numeracy learners, and selected our sample accordingly.

The research was undertaken in learning contexts throughout England, including adult numeracy, Return to Employment, Foundation ICT, family numeracy, GCSE, workplace-based groups, JobcentrePlus, a prison and a 'vocational taster' numeracy course for young people with learning difficulties, in both day and evening classes. Providers included FE colleges, a neighbourhood college, a community group, the Army, a prison, a local education authority (LEA) and a private training provider.

Classes to act as research sites were sought through advertising but when this produced only one site, this was supplemented by sites found through professional contacts. As a result, sites were clustered near to the six teacher-researchers and the core research team in north Lancashire, Gloucestershire and London, with additional sites in Kent, Cambridgeshire and the South-West. Our sample was thus neither random nor fully comprehensive and representative – for example, we were not able to include any learndirect provision, nor did we find as many classes as we would have liked in which numeracy is taught as part of another subject. However, that said, settings were selected so as broadly to reflect the range of settings nationally and the proportion of learners studying in such settings. More than two million of the 2.4 million people who took up *Skills for Life* courses between April 2001 and July 2004 studied in FE (House of Commons Committee of Public Accounts, 2005); the number studying numeracy is not separately identified. We also did not seek to recruit either especially high- or low-performing teachers, but because of the predominance of settings found through personal contacts, the sample is likely to include a higher than average proportion of experienced teachers in established classes. We hope that our sample may be reasonably representative of the teaching workforce, although since all teachers were in a sense volunteers, there may be some bias towards those who are more effective. However, since there is little reliable evidence on the nature and qualifications of those teaching numeracy and non-specialist mathematics to adults, it is impossible to judge the representativeness of the teachers in our study.

A total of 412[2] learners participated in the study, and we observed 34 teachers and 47 classes, 17 in Phase 1 (2003/04) and 30 in Phase 2 (2004/05). Thirty-one of these classes were in FE colleges (11 classes of 16 to 19-year-olds and 20 classes with adults, including ESOL, ICT, etc.), four in adult/neighbourhood colleges, two in family numeracy, four in workplaces, two Jobcentre Plus, one Army training course, two in prisons and one private training provider. More than half of the 47 classes (66 per cent, n=31) were based in FE colleges. By comparison, 73 per cent of all *Skills for Life* numeracy learners (n=265,846) were in FE nationally in 2003/04 and 79 per cent were 19 or older (Learning & Skills Council, 2005).

Class sizes ranged from one to 23 learners, with an average size of eight. A minority of the classes observed (28 per cent) had a learning support assistant or volunteer. Most classes were in the daytime, though around 13 per cent started in the evening; sessions lasted for between one and three hours, with an average of just under two hours.

Phase 1 was used to develop our research instruments, which we trialled extensively at the outset of the project. In both phases 1 and 2, we assessed learners at the beginning[3], Time 1 (T1), and near the end, Time 2 (T2), of their learning programmes, undertook systematic observations of teaching sessions, surveyed learners' attitudes to numeracy, interviewed all teachers and a sample of learners and gathered background information on all learners and teachers. (A note on issues of ethnicity, nationality and language is given in Appendix B). A total of 250 learners took the assessment at both T1 and T2, and 243 completed the attitude survey at both times. We included only those classes where more than 30 hours of tuition were planned. However, because of the intermittent nature of work in workplace settings, this was not always achieved. The average number of hours attended between pre- and post-assessment for each class was 39.

As well as taking a correlative approach to the quantitative data, in order to investigate possible factors associated with effective practice the project has also provided a more detailed qualitative description of teacher and learner attitudes and experiences to assist with insight into causation. These descriptions are largely based on in-depth, semi-structured interviews involving a total of 112 learners and 34 teachers. A summary of data is given below:

---

2 This figure is based on data from the learner background survey.
3 In phase 1, the first assessment (T1) was in January 2004 in classes that started in September 2003. This means we will have missed any learning that took place between these dates.

Table 2.1 **Summary of data collected from 47 numeracy classes 2004–05**

Number of:	Phase 1		Phase 2		Total
	Time 1	Time 2	Time 1	Time 2	
Classes	17	15	30	30	47 (=17+30)
Assessments	131	85	284	165	250 (=85+165)
Attitude	132	88	283	166	243[4]
Background	130		282		412
Observations	29 (1–2 per class)		84 (1–4 per class)		113
Teachers interviewed	16		23[5]		39[6]
Learners interviewed	53		59		112
Teacher background information	16		24		40

The assessment instrument consisted of 20 items from the national *Skills for Life Survey*, in multiple-choice format and from a range of curriculum areas and difficulty levels, from Entry level 1 to Level 2. The attitude survey consisted of 17 statements to which the learners had to respond, again in multiple-choice format. The statements were based around three areas relating to numeracy: enjoyment, usefulness and difficulty of learning.

The intention was to observe each class between two and four times, although for various reasons this was not always possible. During 113 visits, researchers wrote a narrative account and completed detailed schedules recording each teacher's pedagogical approaches.

Ethical considerations

We followed the guidelines of the British Educational Research Association (BERA, 2003; revised 2004). On visits to classes, we gave each learner an information sheet about the project (with contact details), stressing that participation was voluntary. We told them all names would be anonymised and they could withdraw from the project at any time.

4 243 is the number of learners who completed the attitude survey at T1 and T2 in both phases
5 One teacher was not interviewed due to technical difficulties
6 Five teachers were interviewed in both phases

3 Teacher and learner characteristics

This chapter provides detailed background information on the teachers and the learners in the study.

3.1 Teacher profiles

Of the 34 teachers, 25 (74 per cent) were women and nine (26 per cent) were men. Eleven taught classes in Phase 1 only, 18 in Phase 2 only, and five taught classes in both phases. Background data on the teachers was collected through a short self-completed questionnaire.

The mean number of years of teaching experience in numeracy or maths was just over 13, while the vast majority of teachers reported experience of teaching on programmes at Levels 1 and 2 and GCSE and of learners over the age of 19. More than 66 per cent had experience of teaching in secondary schools and 24 per cent in primary schools.

Twenty-seven (79 per cent) of the 34 teachers reported having a formal qualification in mathematics or a related subject, such as science). Thirty teachers (88 per cent) reported having a teaching qualification. Six (18 per cent) of the teachers said they had the new Level 4 qualification for teaching numeracy to adults.

3.2 Learners' profiles

Background data on the learners were collected through a short self-completed questionnaire, as shown in Tables 3.1 to 3.4 below.

Learners were fairly equally gender-balanced. They were of all ages but predominantly in the younger groups, with 40 per cent between 16 and 19.

Table 3.1 **Learners' background characteristics: gender and age**

		% of Overall Sample (n=412)
Gender	Male	46.1
	Female	53.9
Age Group (yrs)	16–19	40.5
	20–29	19.9
	30–39	18.7
	40–49	12.1
	50–59	4.9
	Over 59	2.2

More than 40 per cent of learners reported their ethnic group as British, with the second largest group being Bangladeshi. Almost three out of five learners in the sample reported English as their first language. A variety of languages was reported as additional (second and/or third) languages[7], including English, cited by 28 per cent of learners.

---

7 Details of the characteristics of the full sample are given in the long report which is to be posted on the NRDC website www.nrdc.org.uk

Table 3.2 **Learners' background characteristics: ethnicity and first language**

		Percentage of overall sample (n=412)
Ethnicity	British	41.5
	Bangladeshi	23.5
	Asian other	7.3
	Caribbean	6.4
	African	5.4
	Other	15.9
First Language	English	59.0
	Bengali	20.6
	Other	20.4

Forty per cent of the sample reported being in full-time education, and approximately 15 were employed full-time. Around one in 10 reported being permanently sick or disabled.

Table 3.3 **Learners' characteristics: occupational status**

		Percentage of overall sample (n=412)
Occupational Status	Full-time employed	15.3
	Part-time employed	11.9
	Unemployed	10.4
	Full-time education	40.8
	Permanently sick/ Disabled	10.2
	On Educational Maintenance Allowance (EMA)	8.5
	Other	10.0

The average age learners left schools was 16. Almost 40 per cent of learners reported already holding at least one maths or numeracy qualification, with some previously having attended numeracy classes[8].

Table 3.4 **Learners' characteristics: education and training**

	Sample (n=412)
Mean age left school (years)	16.0
Numeracy class attended since school (percentage)	18.9
Numeracy training at work (percentage)	9.2

In total, 93 learners (nearly 23 per cent of the sample) reported at least one factor that adversely affected their ability to learn. Dyslexia was most frequently mentioned, with around 7 per cent of the sample citing this.

3.3 Summary

The teachers were generally experienced and well-qualified, but this is perhaps not surprising given that they all volunteered to take part. Although there are some biases, inasmuch as there were a large number of Bangladeshi learners, overall learners covered a wide spread and may be more typical of the adult numeracy learner population.

---

8 Details of the qualifications of the full sample are given in the long report.

4 The learners and their experiences

This chapter is concerned with the learners' experiences of learning numeracy from their point of view. It draws on qualitative data from classroom observations and narratives from in-depth interviews, which give an insight into the learners' worlds.

Researchers conducted 61 interviews including 112 learners in 38 different settings, which represented just over a quarter of the total sample. A semi-structured interview schedule was used, which meant that researchers did not ask every learner exactly the same questions.

The data are organised under the following themes: the differences between learning numeracy as a child and adult; motivations for attending the course; attitudes towards numeracy; views about the course; and perceptions of what makes a good numeracy teacher. We have interrogated data using variables of gender, age (adult/16 to 19-year-olds) and level of the course learners were working at (Entry level / Levels 1 and 2), although we have not generally found any major differences between responses.

The breakdown of the interview sample is as follows:

Table 4.1 **The sample of learners interviewed**

Gender	Level	Age
Female: 58 (54 per cent)	Levels 1 & 2: 60 (59 per cent)	Over 19: 69 (64 per cent)
Male: 50 (46 per cent)	Entry levels: 42 (41 per cent)	16–19: 39 (36 per cent)
Missing data: 4	Missing data: 10	Missing data: 4

4.1 Differences between learning numeracy as a child and as an adult

Although many learners said they quite enjoyed their overall time at school, most found learning mathematics 'boring' or 'difficult'. Therefore, many adults spoke of their feelings of anxiety about returning to learning to study numeracy, and most of these were women. However, not all learners had worries and this was particularly true of the 16 to 19-year-olds, who in many cases were, in effect, continuing at school, sometimes among their own peer group.

Many learners contrasted school tuition with their current experience of numeracy teaching, highlighting the smaller classes and the amount of individual attention: 'I've probably had more individual attention learning maths than I've ever had before.' Many learners also cited the relaxed atmosphere, their feelings of security and of not being afraid to make a mistake, the lack of pressure from teachers and peers, the feeling of making progress, and the generally stimulating level of work. Many learners told us that one of the best things about the course was that it was not like school; they also reminded us that they were making a choice, and that is the big difference from compulsory schooling. They also now had the motivation to learn.

Tony: *When I was in school I was useless, and I didn't want to learn it. But now I want to learn it, that's why I came here.*

A key theme that emerged from the learner interviews was that, where the teaching is good, learners begin to understand more about numeracy/maths, and with understanding comes enjoyment and greater confidence:

Anne: *I understand more about maths, but also, Vicky has made me feel so confident about maths. I've never felt so good about maths, and for the first time ever I can now say I enjoy maths. And that's quite a new, big, thing for me.*

We speculate that increased confidence and greater levels of understanding are likely to lead to faster rates of learner progress.

4.2 Motivations for joining and continuing to attend the course

The data in this section come from two sources. A questionnaire-type format was completed by 412 learners as part of their background information and a further subset of 90 also talked about their motivations in greater depth during interview.

Table 4.2 **Learners' reasons for taking current numeracy course**

Reason for doing course	Percentage of overall sample (n=412)
To get a qualification	57.5
To get a better job	42.5
To prove something to myself	37.4
To help me become more confident	37.1
To help children with homework	20.1
To help with everyday things outside the classroom	20.4

Because learners in the questionnaire were allowed to select more than one response, the figures do not total 100 per cent. Research has established that learners' motivations for joining, and continuing to attend, numeracy classes are actually many, intricate and often overlapping (Ecclestone, 2003). Table 4.2 shows that most learners reported 'getting a qualification' as the main reason for doing a numeracy course, with 'getting a better job' being the second most popular response; clearly these two reasons are closely linked. When the reasons were broken down by age, we found that more than twice the number of adults over 20 said that they wanted to study numeracy to prove something to themselves; become more confident; or help with their lives outside the classroom, as against the 16–19 cohort. More obviously, more than three times the number of older adults cited helping their children over the younger group.

In common with other findings (see Swain et al., 2005), these data confirm that learners wanting to prove to themselves that they can succeed in a high-status subject is also a powerful reason. Although giving educational support to their children comes only fifth in the list above, it should be remembered that more than 40 per cent of the sample were aged 16–19, and so would not have children of school age. The research also confirms that only one-fifth of learners attended numeracy courses because they perceived that they lacked skills in their everyday lives.

When asked the same question during interview, 90 learners gave reasons which turned out to be multiple and more complex than the quantitative analysis suggested. The major categories that emerged from the qualitative data were:

1. For myself: to improve knowledge of maths; keep my brain active; to fill in spare time; for enjoyment (25 responses)
2. To provide greater options, for either future study or employment (16 responses)
3. To get a qualification, either for a particular course or job (14 responses)
4. To give educational support to my children (14 responses)
5. To get a better job or to help with my current employment (12 responses)
6. Compelled to by employer (12 responses, including eight learners in the Army)
7. Numeracy is a compulsory part of another course such as literacy or IT (12 responses)
8. To help with everyday life outside the classroom (nine responses)
9. To prove that I can succeed and overcome feelings of embarrassment or lack of knowledge/ability (eight responses).

Some categories overlap and the number of responses was sometimes affected by interviewers' queries.

Once again, there were differences between adults and those aged 16–19. In addition to the older adults saying that they wanted to study numeracy to help their children, many more adults also said it was for themselves; to prove to themselves they could succeed; and to help in everyday life. The 16 to19-year-old learners, however, tended to say that they did not have the choice to study numeracy. This was because their employers told them to, because numeracy was a subsidiary of another course, or because they were paid to attend through Educational Maintenance Allowances (EMAs).

It was almost exclusively female learners who cited the reason of helping their children; and it was mainly learners studying at entry level who said that they wanted to improve their maths and feel more confident with the basics.

Policy-makers often assume that a major reason why people ought to attend numeracy courses is to help them function more effectively in the outside world (see DfEE, 1999). This research, however, as with a previous study (Swain et al., 2005), suggests that this was perceived by learners as being a comparatively minor reason. Most learners said that they could get by with the maths they already knew, although this does not negate the possibility that they would be able to function more effectively after attending a numeracy class.

Researcher: *Do you think you've got enough maths to get by in life?*

Sarah: *If I never come again, I would still be fine.*

4.3 Attitudes and dispositions towards numeracy

From the 77 learners who spoke about their feelings towards numeracy, more than twice the number of learners reported that they liked or enjoyed numeracy (44 per cent, n=34) against those who told us they disliked it or found it boring (21 per cent, n=16). A further 19 per cent (n=15) thought that the subject was OK, and the rest did not give a clear answer.

Findings from the attitude survey (taken at T1 and T2) were even more positive: from a total sample of 243, a large majority reported that they enjoyed numeracy learning (78 per cent, n=190), and only 22 per cent (n=53) stated that they did not enjoy it. These figures remained broadly stable throughout the course, though there was a slight increase in those enjoying numeracy by the end. The same proportion of learners had a positive attitude towards the usefulness of maths (78 per cent, n=232).

It was noticeable that, during the interviews, more than one in four learners (27 per cent, n= 21) said that they were feeling more confident with maths now that they were on the course. This was also reflected in data from the attitude survey, where the most positive shift between the start and end of the course was towards the ease of learning numeracy. We would posit that this growing confidence was often linked to a deepening conceptual understanding that came from seeing connections once barriers had been lifted.

Researcher: *So how did you use to feel about learning maths?*

Jill: *Boring.*

Researcher: *Why?*

Jill: *Didn't understand it.*

Researcher: *What about now?*

Jill: *I love it. It's a challenge.*

Researcher: *That's fantastic.*

Jill: *It's a challenge. It is like playing a game, and once you have learned the rules the game is easy to play.*

Succeeding in what many learners perceive as being a high-status subject also increased self-esteem. It was like joining an elite club (see Dowling, 1998); as one learner put it, 'it makes me feel like an educated person'. The point is further illustrated in the two quotations below:

Cilla: *I feel equal. When I'm at work now I don't still feel that I'm a second-rate person any more. I don't feel that I have to prove myself any more.*

Matt: *To be able to do, like when you see maths, and to be able to do it, it makes me so proud, I am going somewhere. And I want to do more.*

However, in some cases learners were also beginning to see maths in new ways:

Researcher: *So has your attitude towards maths changed since you started doing the classes?*

Sam: *Oh yes, yes. Yeah, yeah. You think diff... You look at things differently and um, you know...*

Researcher: *New ways of looking at maths?*

Sam: *Yes. It's just not all one straight line now, you ... There's so many different ways that I can do now, that I didn't think I could.*

4.4 Views on the course

Learners were asked about their general feelings towards the course, and what they considered to be their favourite and least favourite parts. They were overwhelmingly positive about the course, with more than 90 per cent (n=91) expressing a high level of satisfaction. Only two learners mentioned anything negative. Learners seemed to like most the relaxed atmosphere and the way they were treated as an adult; the individual help and attention; the friendliness of the other learners; working with, and helping other learners; the teacher and the way numeracy was taught; feelings of progress and achievement; and the improvement in their confidence and general self-esteem.

Learning numeracy itself was certainly important for the great majority. Some said that the best thing was 'learning maths'; others stressed it was the sense of achievement they gained from it, and that they felt they were 'getting somewhere' and making progress.

4.5 Perceptions of what makes a good numeracy teacher

Effective practice is likely to be linked to perceptions of good teaching. We asked the learners to say, in general terms, what they thought makes a good teacher: 'What would they be like?' and 'What kinds of things would they do?' We also put the question the other way round: 'What are the characteristics of a bad teacher?' Many learners were very clear about the qualities they felt a good numeracy teacher should have.

Learners felt that the role of the teacher in the numeracy classroom was critical. Teaching consists of a series of relationships, and good relations between the learner and teacher were seen as crucial if effective learning were to take place.

Denise: *Being able to get on with your tutor as friends, as well, makes it a hell of a lot easier. Because if you don't like someone you don't want to be there.*

Learners also recognised that teachers needed to be competent if effective learning is to take place.

Paul: *If you've got good teachers you'll learn. But if you haven't then you are not going to learn, are you?*

Many learners also stressed that it was important that they were treated by a teacher as an adult, 'who talks to you like you are a grown-up, not like you are stupid or whatever.'

Altogether, 83 learners responded to the question of what makes a good teacher, and we give below a summary of their main points. In terms of frequency, the most common response was that the best teacher was one who could explain things clearly. Many of these are similar to those found in an earlier study, *Beyond the Daily Application: making numeracy teaching meaningful to adult learners* (Swain et al., 2005). In order of frequency, a good teacher was described as someone who:

- Has good communication skills; explains things clearly using a number of different ways, including breaking concepts down into small steps (31 responses)
- Has good relations with learners: respects learners; does not make them feel stupid; is approachable and listens carefully to their needs (25 responses)
- Makes maths interesting by being imaginative and makes sure there is plenty of variety in each session. Does not lecture and talk too much (10 responses)
- Gives individual help (seven responses)
- Does not rush through the work (five responses)
- Has a firm grasp of their subject (four responses).

Although 'a firm grasp of their subject' was not seemingly perceived by learners as being that important, it is implicitly connected to 'good communication skills' (which came top); after all, it is highly unlikely that a teacher would be able to 'explain things clearly' without secure subject knowledge. Learners also mentioned several personal qualities and traits which they thought were important. They wanted a teacher who was cheerful, had a sense of humour, was relaxed and easy-going and made them feel welcome. Above all, they wanted someone who was patient (18 responses).

Learners appreciated that at least some teachers were aware of the need to use a variety of resources, and that some used them in particularly imaginative ways. Other learners told us how much they liked playing games, including various sorting activities ('I could have played it forever'), and how much they learned from them. Some learners complained that they grew bored when asked to regularly go through a series of worksheets.

Researcher: *Is there anything you remember doing quite a lot of in class?*

Dave: *Worksheets.*

Researcher: *And how do you feel about that?*

Dave: *It's good to a certain extent. But after a while... I don't know if it's the same with everybody, but after a while, if I just have sheet after sheet after sheet put in front of me, I just sit there and look at it, and lose my train of concentration. I just switch off, if I'm given sheet after sheet after sheet because there's no variation in it.*

Those learners we spoke to thought a poor teacher was someone who:

- Does not explain work but just gives learners work and lets them get on with it (10 responses)
- Is rude and abusive (nine responses)
- Rushes through work, expecting learners to understand the procedure the first time (five responses)
- Does not listen (five responses)
- Does not show interest in their learners' needs (four responses).

Once again, teachers' explanations (in this case the lack of them) top the list. Although learners recognised that there were unequal power relations, in the sense that they expected to come to class to learn numeracy from teachers who knew more than they did, they wanted to be treated as grown-ups, and did not want a teacher who was too bossy and authoritarian. As Betty said, describing a 'bad teacher': it is 'someone who dominates a classroom instead of giving advice. I am who I am and you will do it.'

4.6 Summary

The data suggest that once learners are able to overcome their initial anxieties, both about the course and about mathematics, and when blocks and barriers are lifted, numeracy courses can have a significant and positive effect on their identities – how they view themselves, who they think they are, and who they think they might become. This is both in general terms of improving people's confidence and self-esteem, and in specific terms of their identity as people who can do mathematics. Some people in this study have been able to develop new aspirations and form new dispositions to learning. However, as this study provides only a snapshot, we are unable to speculate either on how related these changes are to specific learning settings, or how enduring they may be.

5 Learners' progress

This chapter begins by considering the criteria used to measure learners' progress. It then reports on the progress learners made. We describe relations between learners' progress and their background characteristics (such as gender and ethnicity) and in relation to their teachers' characteristics (such as their teaching experience and level of qualification). After reporting learners' attitudes, and the changes that occurred, the chapter ends by considering the relationship between learners' attitudes and the characteristics of teachers and learners.

5.1 What counts as progress?

Learners' average progress in each class, as measured by the average gain in their scores on the assessment instrument between T1 and T2, is used to judge the effectiveness of teaching and learning in this and the other NRDC effective practice studies, as it was in the study on which these projects are based (Condelli, 2001). However, it is important that our findings on learners' progress are not over-interpreted. For instance, for some (including older adults, adults with specific learning difficulties or those with poor memories), to simply maintain their level of skills in numeracy rather than falling back is itself a sign of personal progress (Schuller et al., 2002). We also know that regress is an effect of time out of work for many people (Bynner and Parsons, 1998) and learners may be particularly vulnerable to regress if they are not regularly using the skills assessed in the study outside the classroom.

It should be noted that there are ways of monitoring progress other than gains in attainment on a standard instrument. For instance, using a more detailed customised assessment for each class which was more closely linked to the curriculum taught, monitoring changes in learners' actions in the classroom, or asking the learners themselves (see Sections 4.4–4.6). These separately or in combination may have provided a more accurate picture.

We are also aware that our chosen assessment instrument was not as valid and reliable as we would have liked in assessing progress, especially among the full range of learners in our study. We needed to find items which had already been trialled reasonably successfully with a comparable sample, assembled into a test which was sensitive to learning on a small timescale, but which also covered a wide range of learners and could be administered quickly and efficiently in different settings without taking too much time away from, sometimes limited, teaching time. It proved difficult to satisfy these different requirements simultaneously and we believe that the degree of sensitivity achieved in accurately measuring gains in learning is considerably less than we would ideally have wanted (see also Section 8.2).

The items were selected from those used in the *Skills for Life* Survey after studying the performance data; some were amended slightly after trialling. The 20 items were all multiple-choice, incorporated a high proportion of photographs and diagrams, with only simple text, and were presented one per page. An example of an Entry level 2 question is shown below (see Figure 5.1).

Figure 5.1 **An example of an assessment item**

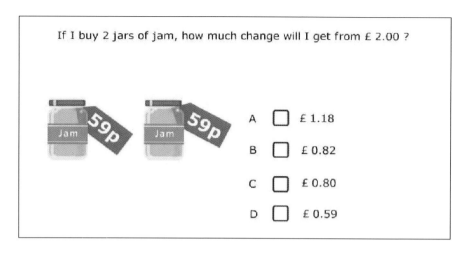

Researchers administered the test and were able to read or explain the meaning of questions for ESOL learners or those with language difficulties. Calculators were available on request but were seldom used. Tests took about 30–40 minutes, but learners were often free to take longer.

5.2 Gains in numeracy attainment measured between two time points

Of the 412 learners in both phases of the study, 250 completed an assessment at both time points, towards the beginning and end of their numeracy course. This represents a retention rate of 60.5 per cent. Not all of the learners absent at T2 had left the course; some were simply absent on the day of the assessment. In this section we are presenting data only on learners assessed at both time points.

This group of 250 was compared with the 162 assessed at T1 only in terms of a range of background characteristics to establish that the two groups did not differ significantly. If that were the case, the assessment data shown below could have been biased. The two groups were compared by gender, age group, age they left school, qualifications held and factors affecting learning, as well as by their T1 assessment score. There were no significant differences between the groups in any of these variables.

The total percentage scores and standard deviations on the test for the 250 learners who completed the assessment tests at both time periods (T1 and T2) are presented in Table 5.1 below. (The same test was used at both times.)

Table 5.1 **Learner assessment data**

	T1		T2		Gain		
	Mean % score	S. D.	Mean % score	S. D.	Mean % gain	S.D.	Effect size
Phase 1 (n=85)	43.8	24.8	51.6	26.7	7.8*	16.5	0.31
Phase 2 (n=165)	45.5	19.5	55.6	23.2	10.1**	17.06	0.52

* significant at p<0.05), ** significant p<0.001

It can be seen from the table that there was approximately an average 9 per cent gain between the two time points across all learners in Phases 1 and 2. The mean gains are statistically significant with reasonably high effect sizes, and in a test with 20 items it is equivalent to an average learner being able to answer correctly two additional questions in the final test administration. This is perhaps more significant than it sounds, as there were only four questions at each of the five levels. This increase might be thought to be due to a testing effect, given that the same test was used both times. It is true that the learners were clearly more familiar with the form of the test on the second occasion, but generally we feel that the two events were so far apart in time, usually with a gap of seven or eight months, for it to be unimportant that the items were the same.

The average number of teaching hours learners received between T1 and T2 was 39. However, there was also no correlation between number of hours attended and the gain in score between T1 and T2 (Spearman's rho = −0.03, p = 0.7). This finding seems counter-intuitive and inconsistent with other research results. However, this may reflect particular circumstances. For example, one of the shortest courses, the week-long course run by the Army, was also very intensive and there was strong pressure on learners to succeed in the test at the end of the week. In contrast, some learners who had difficulty in learning joined two numeracy courses and so the number of hours attended was extremely high, without any compensating gain. The finding also seems inconsistent with the smaller average gains made in Phase 1, where the time elapsing between tests, and the number of attended hours between them, was smaller. However, the reduction in gains in Phase 1 may be because the first test was some way into the course in many cases, and hence we may have lost the benefit of large rises in the early weeks of the course, when learner confidence and regained familiarity with mathematics are both likely to be growing quickly.

In interpreting results such as these we need constantly to bear in mind the difference between *correlation* and *causation.* For example, longer learning time would be expected to cause greater progress, and the difference between Phase 1 and Phase 2 results supports that, but there may be other underlying associations which explain the lack of correlation. Conversely, a significant correlation between a type of teaching approach and gains made does not necessarily suggest that the approach causes the gains; both may be associated with a third factor.

Table 5.2 shows the mean gains made by each class; these are shown in rank order within each phase. These are presented like this so that the wide distribution of mean gains in each class can be appreciated. For example, it can be seen from Table 5.2 that there is a large spread in the mean class gains, with the largest at more than 30 per cent and the lowest at −13. The table also indicates the relatively small number of learners in many classes present to be tested on both occasions.

It should be noted that negative mean gains do not necessarily indicate that learners knew less at the end of the course than at the start. These indicate only that the mean scores on a small sample of items were lower. Small negative differences may be within the bounds of random test error. Larger negative differences arise only with very small groups of up to three learners and may reflect some idiosyncratic factor related to one individual or to the different circumstances in which the two assessments were taken.

Table 5.2 **Mean gain of classes in Phases 1 and 2 in rank order**

Phase 1 classes			Phase 2 classes		
Rank order	Mean gain %	Number of learners assessed	Rank order	Mean gain %	Number of learners assessed
1	27.04	9	1	32.50	5
2	13.89	6	2	31.11	6
3	13.34	5	3	23.33	5
4	12.50	6	4	20.00	2
5	9.52	7	5	17.86	7
6	5.56	6	6	16.54	13
7	4.17	4	7	15.56	3
8	3.67	5	8	14.81	9
9	3.18	11	9	14.17	2
10	2.17	10	10	12.50	12
11	1.25	4	11	10.56	3
12	1.15	2	12	10.33	5
13	- 0.33	2	13	9.58	4
14	- 0.67	5	14	9.44	3
15	- 2.77	3	15	9.05	7
			16	8.89	6
			17	7.08	4
			18	6.67	3
			19	6.33	5
			20	6.30	9
			21	6.21	11
			22	4.44	3
			23	3.97	13
			24	3.75	4
			25	2.33	5
			26	1.11	3
			27	-1.11	6
			28	-4.44	3
			29	-12.78	3
			30	-13.33	1

The scatterplot (Figure 5.2) illustrates the mean scores for each class in the two administrations of the test, at times T1 and T2. The diagonal *y=x* line is drawn in for the scatterplot: any class with a data-point on the line had the same mean score both times the test was taken. The further the point is along the line away from the origin, the greater the scores in both test administrations. Any class above this line had a positive gain in the mean class score between T1 and T2, while classes below it had a negative mean gain (the mean class score was lower at the later time T2 than it had been at T1). The further the data-point is away from the *y=x* line and above it, the greater is the gain, and the greater the distance below the line, the greater the loss.

The points corresponding to most classes lie in a narrow band just above the line, indicating similar small gains, whatever the initial mean score at time T1.

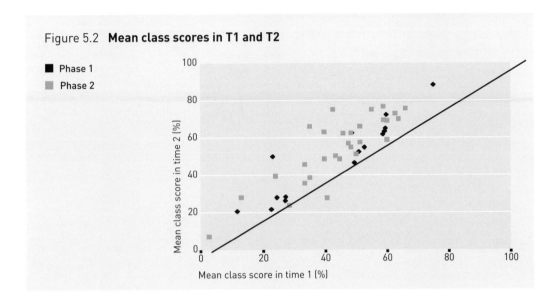

Figure 5.2 **Mean class scores in T1 and T2**

5.3 Relationship between attainment gains and learners' and teachers' background characteristics

A series of univariate analyses (one-way ANOVAs, see Glossary) was carried out first to investigate if any learner characteristics were related to amount of progress made (as measured by gain in scores between T1 and T2). The following variables were examined: gender, age group, first language, ethnic group, having attended another numeracy class since school, reporting a factor affecting learning and formal qualifications held. Table 5.3 below shows the mean gains in scores for each variable, as well as whether the differences are statistically significant. It can be seen that females made on average larger gains than males and that the 30–39 and 40–49 age groups made the smallest gains on average. Learners from non-white ethnic backgrounds also had larger gains. The only statistically significant difference found was that learners who said they lacked a formal qualification in maths made greater progress. There was no correlation between the age participants left school/full-time education and the magnitude of the gain in scores between T1 and T2 (*rho* = −0.04, *p* = 0.4).

Table 5.3 **Mean gains for different groups of learners**

		Mean gain in score* between T1 and T2
Gender	male	5.03
	female	6.04
Age group	16–19	5.29
	20–29	6.02
	30–39	2.73
	40–49	5.2
	50–59	8.92
	Over 59	11.28
First language	English	4.83
	other	5.53
Other numeracy class attended since school	yes	5.00
	no	5.01
Factor affecting learning	yes	6.05
	no	5.42
Qualification held	yes	2.87
	no	7.20
Ethnic group	white	4.75
	other	5.96

* out of 60

The above variables were also entered into a regression model to see whether they could significantly predict progress in numeracy in combination, but no significant results were found.

We also explored differences in progress in terms of the reasons learners had stated as their main motivation for doing the course, given as part of their background information (see Section 4.3). As participants could select more than one such reason, these had to be treated as separate variables. The only statistical difference found was between learners who stated that they wanted to become more confident as opposed to those who did not. The former group had a mean gain of eight points, while the latter had a mean gain of four points. This difference was significant at $p < 0.05$. Another large difference was between learners who stated that they wanted to get a better job and those who did not. Again, the former group made more progress (mean gain of just under eight points) compared to the latter (mean gain of four points). This difference approached but did not reach statistical significance ($p = 0.06$).

Finally, there were no significant correlations between any of the teacher characteristics we measured and the progress of the learners in their class. As explained in Section 3.3, these characteristics included years and type of teaching experience, and teaching and maths qualifications held. This may seem counter-intuitive, but it mirrors other findings about primary teachers and progress in numeracy. For example, it was shown by Askew et al. (1997) that there was not a strong relationship between teachers' formal mathematical qualifications and the depth of their understanding of basic mathematical ideas, although the connectedness of teachers' understanding was related to gains in pupils' learning. Similarly, as with that study, we also found that young and/or inexperienced teachers were not necessarily less effective than older and/or more experienced teachers, possibly because of their more recent training experience.

5.4 Differential gains for different levels and areas of mathematics

Table 5.4 shows the distribution of the items within the assessment in terms of the topics and levels they covered (using the *Skills for Life* classifications). It also shows the initial success rate of learners at T1 for the items in each level and the progress they made at T2. As we have already stated, gains were generally smaller for Phase 1, perhaps because of the shorter time period between T1 and T2 (see Table 5.1). However, the trends in the gains are similar for both groups, and the gain sizes overlap as shown in Table 5.2, so the data from both phases has been combined in Table 5.4 to increase the sample size. The overall mean gain per item was 7.6 per cent, indicating that on an average item nearly 8 per cent more learners were successful at the end than at the start.

Table 5.4 **Number of items in each level and topic with success rates for each level at T1 and T2 and the gain**

Level/topic	Entry 1	Entry 2	Entry 3	Level 1	Level 2	Total Items
Basic money	1	1	1			3
Money calculations		1		1	2	4
Whole numbers and time		1	1			2
Measures and proportion				1	1	2
Weight and scales	1					1
Length and scaling	1		2	1	1	5
Charts and data	1	1		1		3
Number of items	4	4	4	4	4	20
Mean success T1	89.3	79.5	60.3	31.8	23.8	56.9
Mean success T2	92.4	83.5	66.2	43.8	36.6	64.4
Mean gain	3.1	4.0	5.9	12.0	12.8	7.6

A significant correlation was found between the difficulty of the question, as measured by the proportion answering it correctly at T1, and the gain between T1 and T2 in the number of people answering correctly. As the difficulty of the question increased, so the gains made increased (n=20, *rho* = 0.87). One reason for small gains in the Entry level 1 and 2 items is the high proportion of learners who answered correctly in the first assessment, so there was little room for progress in these items. The other reason for the higher gains in Levels 1 and 2 items is that 18 groups were aiming at Levels 1 and/or 2, and just 10 were aiming only at Entry or Pre-Entry levels (the remaining 17 were mixed). Moreover, Entry-level classes generally contained fewer learners. Once the level is controlled for, there were no clear differences in gain between the different mathematical topics.

We went on to investigate whether the learners with higher test scores in the first assessment made greater progress. However, this was not so, as indicated by a near zero correlation between learner gains and their test score at T1. In fact, the correlation was weakly negative (n=250, *rho*= −0.15). This suggests that the test design allowed learners from a range of initial attainment levels to make progress, rather than favouring those with either initially high or low attainment. Because of the earlier finding that the harder items rise most, it would seem that the gains made by learners with lower scores must be mainly on the harder items.

5.5 Changes in learners' attitudes

A total of 415 learners completed the 'attitude to numeracy' questionnaire at T1 and 254 at T2, with a total of 243 learners completing it at both time-points over the two years of the project. Statistics in this section therefore refer to those 243 learners, unless otherwise specified.

From the 17 statements, learners had to tick one of four options from 'strongly disagree' to 'strongly agree'. The questionnaire was designed to include statements relating to usefulness, enjoyment and difficulty of learning numeracy. Again, it is not clear that the instrument, because of limits on length, could be sufficiently valid and sensitive to accurately monitor changes in attitude, of the type noted in the report of qualitative data in Chapter 4.

A factor analysis of the items in the questionnaire did not yield any stable or interpretable factors. Reliability coefficients (Cronbach's alpha) were quite high, 0.77 and 0.80 respectively for T1 and T2, suggesting that the instrument was a measure of one underlying factor, of positive or negative feelings and attitudes towards mathematics/numeracy. We have therefore analysed the data from the attitudes instrument in two ways and present them separately below. First, we treated the 17 items in the instrument as forming one 'attitudes' variable; second, we split the items into three groups, corresponding to the three sub-scales: enjoyment, usefulness and difficulty. This grouping was theory-led rather than data-driven, given the inconclusive results of the factor analysis referred to above.

Analysis of overall attitude scores

Scores on the single unidimensional scale could range from a minimum of 17 (indicating a very positive attitude to numeracy) to a maximum of 68 (indicating a very negative attitude). Table 5.5 below presents descriptive statistics of this attitudes score at both time points (combining data from Phases 1 and 2). The average score on the scale was slightly lower at the second time point, which indicates that attitudes were on the whole *more positive* at the end of the course than at the beginning. Although numerically small, this gain was significant, t (242) = 2.47, p = 0.01.

Table 5.5 **Descriptive statistics for attitude scale**

	Mean score	Standard deviation	Cronbach's alpha
T1	37.4	6.6	0.77
T2	36.4	6.8	0.80

The correlations between attainment and attitude scores, at both time points, were weak and non-significant, as was the correlation of gains in assessment and attitude scores. These seem surprising findings; one might expect that those with higher scores would be more positive about mathematics and that learners demonstrating a positive change in attitudes would make most progress. It may have been that the attitude survey was not capable of detecting the increased confidence and enthusiasm for mathematics that we experienced in interviewing some learners. Furthermore, there is often a complex relationship between attitude and attainment; for example, in international comparisons of mathematical attainment there is usually a negative correlation between the mean attitude and attainment scores across different countries, since more difficult programmes may achieve higher scores but leave learners less confident. In our study, it could be that some programmes which move forward very slowly and concentrate on consolidation do help to boost confidence, a key factor for many adults, and hence raise attitude scores, but do not necessarily achieve large measured gains in attainment.

Analysis of attitude sub-scales

As explained above, the 17 items of the attitude questionnaire were also divided into three groups, according to the particular aspects of attitudes towards numeracy they intended to measure, namely perceived usefulness (seven statements), enjoyment (five statements) and difficulty (five statements). There were small changes in all three dimensions, all in the expected direction; that is, learners found numeracy more useful, more enjoyable and less difficult at the end of the course. The change between scores at T1 and T2 on the sub-scale of difficulty was also statistically significant, $t(242) = 2.91$, $p < 0.01$. This suggests that learners came to see numeracy as a little less difficult as a result of their course.

5.6 Relations between learners' attitudes and their characteristics

To see whether there were any significant differences between different groups of learners, we examined the attitude data according to gender, age and ethnicity. No statistically significant differences were found between female and male learners. However, learners aged 20 or older did have a significantly more positive attitude towards numeracy learning than those aged 16–19 both at the start and the end of the course, $F(5, 229) = 4.08$, $p < 0.001$.

It was also found that, at the start of the course, those from non-white ethnic backgrounds had a significantly more positive attitude towards numeracy learning than those from white ethnic backgrounds, $t(239) = 2.95$, $p < 0.01$. By the end of the course, though, this difference was no longer significant, indicating that the attitude of learners from white ethnic backgrounds had improved more.

5.7 Summary

Taking all classes together, significant progress was made over the length of the numeracy courses. There was an extremely wide range of mean gains between different classes. There was, however, little association between the size of gains and types of learner, except that those with no previous qualifications and those wanting to become more confident tended to make larger gains. There was no association between gains and teacher characteristics. In contrast, there were small but positive overall changes in attitude. These tended to be greatest for older people, and related particularly to a perception of numeracy as being less difficult.

6 Teachers' practices

Chapter 6 begins by reporting on teachers' perceptions of their numeracy teaching; it continues with a description of the characteristics or features that were found in the classrooms; and concludes by introducing the notion of teaching typologies.

6.1 Teachers' perceptions of numeracy teaching

This section describes teachers' perceptions of teaching numeracy to adults. Themes have been chosen from the interviews to reflect some of the issues that are identified in this study, and also to recognise that adult learners comprise a diverse population. Teachers describe what they believe to be the features of an effective lesson, how they organise the learners and structure their lessons. Selections have been made to try to represent a cross-section of teachers' views. The data are taken from interviews with teachers in both phases. Thirty-three of the 34 teachers were interviewed, some more than once.

Learner populations

Teachers talked about issues around teaching adult education classes generally. In some classes the range of ability was relatively small; in other classes the wide range of ability was perceived as problematic. For instance, Brenda said that she found that it was 'very difficult' to give learners, who ranged from Entry level 1 to Level 3, the individual attention they needed. However, it was possible to get learners to work well together even if the differences in ability level were wide. As Jivanta explained, learners in her class all seemed to work well together, even though they ranged in ability from Entry level 2 to Level 2. The group was observed as being 'busy', with a good atmosphere and attendance record. Learners were seen to get on well together and to help each other.

Even classes working at a similar level were not necessarily completely homogeneous, since an individual might be strong in one curriculum area but relatively weak or have a learning difficulty in another area. This is commensurate with the Government's description of adult learners as having 'spiky profiles' (DfES, 2001).

Hugh: *You have a mix of learners who are Entry level 3 in certain skills, a certain number of skills, and Entry... Pre-Entry in other areas... I mean, that's the difficulty, because you will have somebody like Max who is quite capable in some areas, and yet will find it very difficult to maybe measure something.*

Other classes had distinctive populations, such as classes for learners with learning difficulties and ESOL classes. A class for people with learning difficulties was described as being quite diverse, with some learners showing little motivation. They would do nothing for a whole lesson, while others would work hard. Some learners had emotional needs, others specific learning difficulties. Their educational experience also varied, as did their potential to make progress and attain at higher levels of mathematics. Some had joined the course from school, others had been school refusers and some had been to special school. Some would go on to an intermediate course and had, according to the teacher, the potential to do GCSE, while others would need to repeat the class the following year. This diversity is illustrated in the following quotation, where Joanna talked about an incident in a recent class involving a male learner who had been asked to leave another course.

Joanna: *Should have seen him last week, actually. He comes up to me and needs his shoelace doing up and thinks I can do his shoelace up. He put his foot up, I did his shoelace up and said: 'There you go' and he bent over to kiss me, it must be what he does to his Mum [laughs]... Personal space! And there, you know, tying one person's shoelace when I've got someone else in my other ear asking me about quadratic equations because the maths exam is on.*

In some types of classes teachers often found it difficult to motivate learners. This problem was particularly acute in classes where numeracy was taught as part of a vocational course or as part of a Basic Skills element of a full-time course. Judy talked of her experience of teaching on a painting and decorating course, and of how learners showed greater motivation when numeracy was related to their potential employment.

Judy: *It's been awful. You know, just trying to keep them in the room. They are a tough bunch. But anyway, I did area and perimeter and of course it was something that they do, and they knew all about it, and their tutor had told them they needed to know all about how much carpeting and ... And all of a sudden I had their attention. When I move on to probability, it will all go out the window.*

Jobseekers' classes also had a distinct population, as they were made up of learners who were long-term unemployed and referred by the Jobcentre. These classes could present particular problems. Some learners attended for eight weeks and others up to six months, which made planning for the class difficult.

Hugh: *Because they are sent by the employment centre, and if they find a job in the meantime they go to the job and they suddenly disappear from us.*

In two particular Jobseekers' classes the majority of learners came from ethnic minority backgrounds. Their teacher, Alex, believed that many would not have volunteered to attend a numeracy class, and some had been coerced by the Jobcentre. He felt, therefore, that it was up to him to create a good, purposeful, working environment, where learners could enjoy themselves and feel they were achieving. In fact, the two classes taught by this Phase 2 teacher, Alex, were in the top three classes in terms of gains. Learners did well despite the difficulties in terms of learner motivations for attending and difficulties with the language. This suggests that the teacher is crucial and can really inspire learners by creating a purposeful and rich learning environment. However, it was also clear that the classes of similarly inspirational teachers did not make much measured progress, perhaps because the learners in their classes found learning very difficult, and maybe had less incentive than unemployed ethnic-minority workers whose mathematical potential was unrealised through previous lack of education.

Features of an effective lesson

Teachers were asked about what they thought made an effective lesson. Features included being flexible and able to use a variety of approaches to accommodate learners' needs, ensuring that learners were engaged in the learning process and developed a positive attitude to the subject. Getting learners to articulate what they had understood was perceived as important, as was enabling them to make connections to other areas of mathematics.

Good planning was mentioned as a key ingredient by some teachers:

Helen: *You need to be planned, you need to have thought through what you are going to deliver. You need to have taken into account the learning styles of the different individuals. You need to have thought about the particular resources that are going to suit those learning styles, that you are not necessarily trying to give everybody exactly the same thing.*

Flexibility was also important, not least because activities sometimes took more or less time to work through than anticipated, and learners worked at different speeds.

In some instances the structure of a lesson could vary according to the teaching focus, as Jivanta explained.

Jivanta: *Depends what we're doing, really. I mean, usually when I'm just working through the scheme of work and we're doing, you know, whole-group activities, I start off with a whole-group activity or something interactive usually, um, whether it's a, you know, pairing game or something, or something on the board where all the learners are involved with it... then, you see it depends on what we're doing. If we're doing something that needs quite a lot of differentiation I'll perhaps give, you know, the Entry learners something that I know they can be getting on with while I sit with the Level 1 and 2 learners and go through their work with them and then I'll kind of switch... or if I can do the introduction that covers all levels, I'll do that and give them all differentiated work after that. Um, and then after the break I either switch to something completely different or do something slightly different within the same topic. Again starting with something, you know, maybe a game or something after the break and then moving to some more practice.*

It was thought important by many teachers to start from where the learners are, and as learners were not all the same, this meant providing a variety of activities, and a range of ways of doing things that incorporated learners' own methods. It was also thought that learners needed to be extended beyond their comfort zone.

Rosemary: *Starting from where the learners are, be aware of that, and pushing them on and extending them, as far as they are comfortable going, probably a bit further. But extending them all as far as they need to go, which is not the same for everybody. A variety of activities and a variety of ways of doing things. Not just doing worksheets after worksheets.*

Learners needed to be engaged, focused on the task, and to be interacting with each other in a meaningful way. According to Becky, to be effective, learning about mathematics should be thought of as a 'social activity'.

Becky: *I think [maths] is a lesson where people take ownership of what they are doing and where they are actually engaged and focused on task almost all the time. Most lessons should also include discussion and talking and debate, and I think a good lesson is one where the learners actually dive into the topic and talk about it, and whatever activities are given to them generate that sort of bouncing off of ideas against each other.*

The importance of learners being actively involved and participating in lessons was echoed by other teachers. This could mean that learners were physically involved, for example by volunteering to write on the board, as well as mentally involved by engaging in the task. Encouraging learners to make their thinking explicit, whether to the teacher or another learner, was also perceived to be of value.

Allowing learners to articulate what they understood was important because it helped learners not only to practise a 'technique', but also to assimilate an underlying concept.

Alex: *Something that allows learners to speak. You have always got to hear learners speak. In numeracy lessons you have got to be both practising techniques and trying to get to the underlying concept behind. So learners need to have a grasp of concept, grasp of what... they are doing and why they are doing it. So in other words, what are the bases of the maths behind it? But also they have got to somehow assimilate the technique. So practice of the technique but without the inbuilt understanding and the underlying concept that could be easily forgotten. You need to have both elements in there.*

Teachers felt that rather than teaching concepts as discrete entities, learners should be made aware of the connectedness of ideas in mathematics so that what is taught is linked coherently with what had been taught before, as well as what would be taught in the future.

Organisation of learners

As will be shown from the observational data in the next section (6.2), teachers organised learners in a number of ways although, as in the reading study, the most common forms were the whole class together or individuals working on their own.

In some instances, the organisation of learners was a management issue. For Becky, class size, with about nine mixed-ability learners, meant that the organisation of learners was regarded as a time-management issue. To make the best use of her time, learners would be taught as a group to begin with, before starting on individualised work. Rheanne, on the other hand, explained she wanted learners to work in groups for practical work, but in pairs or alone for written work. For some teachers, ways of working were relatively fluid and were largely dictated by the nature of the activity.

Becky: *The way I normally do it is to recap on what we have done before, and if I am extending that topic or introducing a new topic I will usually do some sort of starter activity at the beginning of the session, and then either get everybody working in small groups or pairs, or perhaps a group activity that everybody is involved in.*

As Margaret explained, lessons started with some individual work, but also sometimes included group work to give the learners an opportunity to work together on an activity that had some relevance to all learners.

Margaret: *I try to make sure there is something for everybody to do when they come in. Sometimes that is just they haven't finished homework, but I try to have at least one worksheet, whatever, so someone is not sitting waiting, and then try to get to everybody at some point in the lesson. And then we have, occasionally, just so they can work together, in the middle of the session we have done an activity together... I have tended to do something, and intentionally make it something that isn't on their targets, but is appropriate to everybody. So looking through the tests, I did something on shape that would come up for all of them, and could be done at multi-level, really.*

Group work was seen as a way of developing class cohesion, especially among particular groups of learners, such as those in prison. One advantage of small group work, noted by some teachers, was that individuals could use their particular strengths to support one another. However, some potential difficulties with group work were also noted. As one teacher explained, she would sometimes tell one of the more able learners to help another group. She was aware, however, that with lower-ability groups in particular, the more able learner might merely provide the correct answer rather than helping other learners to work out answers for themselves.

In some cases, the structure of the lesson was influenced by the type of course. This was particularly true with the five-day course run by the Army. There was also a problem in a work-based course, where learners came and went at different times throughout a given period. In this instance, coursework tended to be very individualised out of necessity, and although the teacher hoped that it would be possible that learners working on the same topic would be able to work together, this rarely happened.

Other teachers actively favoured independent working. According to Tara, during individualised work the learning experience was enhanced by learners having access to a rich variety of resources including worksheets, textbooks and online materials. Some teachers were keen to have learners actively engaged in carrying out activities together. However this was not always easy, as some learners were reluctant to work with others and preferred to work alone, getting through as much work as possible independently.

Tara: *I have tried to make it as student-centred as possible, trying to get them to work together. But they are such a hard-working group, they just want to work independently. Or they want to get through the work really fast [...] I mean, some people just naturally work together, and some people you have got to make them. I mean, I am trying, but you saw, they just didn't speak once, just working away.*

Teachers in one FE college had been involved in the DfES Standards Unit project *Thinking Through Mathematics*, piloting approaches and materials designed to involve learners by using a range of practical activities which explicitly promote collaborative learning, discussion and reflection (DfES, 2005b). Positive feedback from learners as to how much more interesting these sessions were had convinced many teachers in this college of the value of such methods. Rosemary said that she now thought of herself as a 'facilitator', helping learners to iron out misconceptions, rather than simply imparting knowledge.

Getting learners to articulate their ideas, either to the teacher or another learner, enabled teachers to become aware of learners' misconceptions, because without understanding, no matter how much practice was undertaken, 'the underlying concept... could easily be forgotten'. Questioning learners, often repeatedly, was seen as a good way, not only to find out what they were thinking, but also to help them clarify their ideas.

Rosemary: *I try to ask questions that I think will help to work out what they are doing, where they are at the moment. Clarify to me what they are thinking. And they are supposed to lead them through. Try to get them to identify and clarify things in their mind as well.*

However, knowing the right questions to ask is a skill in its own right and is not always easy, especially with ESOL learners, partly because of the language barrier, but also because some may be more used to being given facts to learn rather than being asked to think for themselves.

These are some of the key points that teachers told us when they were asked what they thought made an effective lesson. These have been drawn out and summarised by us. Features included:

- Being flexible and able to use a variety of approaches in order to accommodate learners' needs; learners work at different speeds, and activities sometimes take more or less time to work through than anticipated
- Enabling learners to make connections to other areas of mathematics
- Good planning, including anticipating learners' responses
- Starting from where the learners are, providing a variety of activities, and a variety of ways of doing things that incorporate learners' own methods
- Extending learners beyond their 'comfort zone'
- Getting learners to interact together, and viewing learning as a social activity
- Encouraging learners to make their thinking explicit to the teacher and to other learners; allowing them to articulate what they understand.

6.2 Classroom characteristics

As we have already noted, a total of 34 teachers were observed in 47 settings[9]. The findings in this section are based on analysis of researchers' reflective observations that were completed retrospectively after each session. The analysis of sessions was divided into seven different aspects:

1. structure/organisation
2. teachers' role
3. teaching process
4. learners and learning
5. teacher-learner relations
6. materials
7. mathematical pedagogy (Phase 2 only).

A numbering system from 0–3 was used to indicate the emphasis the researcher gave each characteristic of the lesson: 0 indicates that it was not observed; 1, that it was observed to a very limited extent; 2, that it was observed to some extent, and 3, that it was observed to a high degree. The reflection sheet therefore allows us to describe the characteristics of the lessons as a whole. Results for each class are based on the average ratings for between one and four session observations, with an average of 2.4 observations over the two phases. A graph showing the average score in each category for all classes is shown at the end of the section.

The first paragraph of each of the following sections summarises the findings. This is followed by a figure showing the percentage of teachers who used each strategy not at all, to a limited extent, to some extent or to a high degree during their classes.

9 Some teachers taught in more than one setting, and some settings had two teachers teaching as part of a job-share arrangement.

Structure and organisation

Few sessions had a mental starter (that is where the whole class developed and practised mental and oral skills) and the majority did not have a final plenary or recap by the teacher of work covered during the lesson. The most common methods of class organisation were to teach the class as a whole group or have individuals working on their own. Overall, very little group work was found, although it was a little more common to find learners working in pairs.

Figure 6.1 **Structure and organisation**

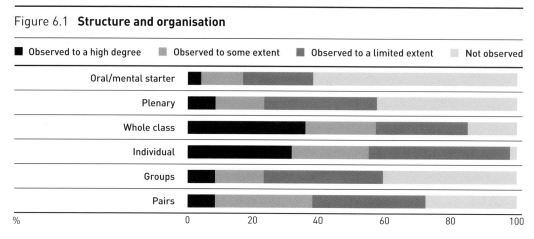

Teacher's role

The great majority of teachers were enthusiastic. They gave both praise and encouragement to their learners, they gave feedback to learners on their work and they monitored learning as it was taking place. Most teachers also used direct teaching, and the majority were flexible and able to respond to learners' needs. Teachers were seen encouraging discussion among learners on a regular basis in about half of the sessions, although less than a third consistently set up collaborative learning.

Figure 6.2 **The teacher's role**

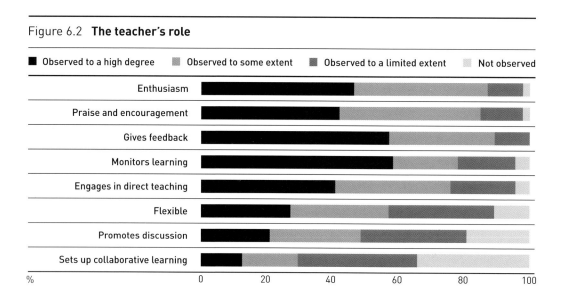

The teaching process

Most teachers demonstrated good subject knowledge, gave clear explanations and worked through examples. The majority used a range of activities and broke down work into smaller steps. Teachers were seen differentiating work, making connections to other areas of mathematics, or asking higher-order questions, in about half the sessions observed.

Figure 6.3 **Teaching process**

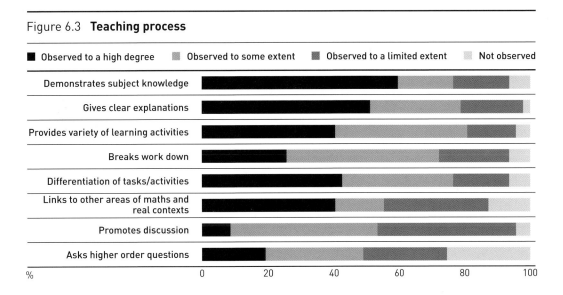

Learning

Learners were engaged in their learning for the majority of the time and were given time by the teachers to gain and develop understanding. Learners were challenged and stretched, or had their individual needs addressed, in about half of the sessions. While learners were seen being given opportunities to discuss an activity, there were fewer occasions when they were judged to be learning from each other during discussions with their peers. There were even fewer opportunities for them to raise their own issues or influence the content of the lesson, and learners' own interests were only rarely incorporated.

Figure 6.4 **Learning**

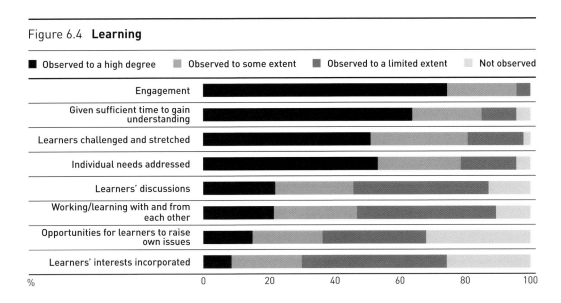

Teacher-learner relations

There was great deal of mutual respect between teachers and learners and most learners felt free to express themselves. Teachers shared the overall goals of the lesson with the learners in about half of the sessions.

Figure 6.5 **Teacher-learner relations**

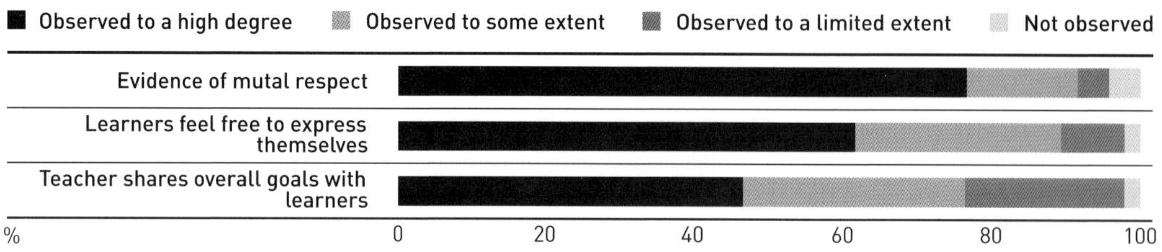

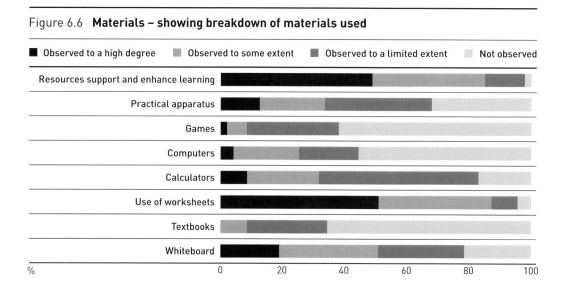

Materials

Resources were judged to have supported and enhanced learning in the majority of sessions. Hardly any teachers used any practical apparatus, games, computers or calculators. While worksheets were used extensively, few teachers used textbooks. Teachers used a plain whiteboard at the front of the class in about a half of the sessions.

Figure 6.6 **Materials – showing breakdown of materials used**

Mathematical pedagogy

This term refers to seven characteristics:

1. *Manipulative:* the teacher uses concrete materials to model numbers (e.g. counting money);
2. *Visual:* the teacher uses pictures or diagrams to aid understanding (e.g. a picture of a cake to show fractions);
3. *Symbolic*: the teacher uses numbers and letters (e.g. 4 + 3 = ?);
4. *Procedural*: the teacher shows learners an algorithm or procedure that is needed to find the answer (e.g. 24 x 7);
5. *Conceptual*: the teacher develops meaning and understanding, making connections to other areas of mathematics (e.g. linking fractions to decimals);
6. *Strategic*: the teacher asks learners to think about how they would solve a problem, (e.g. what instruments/strategies you would need to use to find the height of a door);

7. *Contextual:* the teacher relates mathematics to the world outside the classroom (e.g. creates graphs by using data likely to relate to learners' lives).

The majority of the teachers asked learners to follow procedures using symbols (mainly numbers). There was less emphasis on conceptual understanding or relating topics such as fractions to other areas of mathematics. Although about half of the sessions showed teachers relating mathematical topics to the world outside the classroom, and employing visual techniques to aid understanding, very few teachers asked learners to solve problems or used concrete materials.

Figure 6.7 **Mathematical pedagogy**

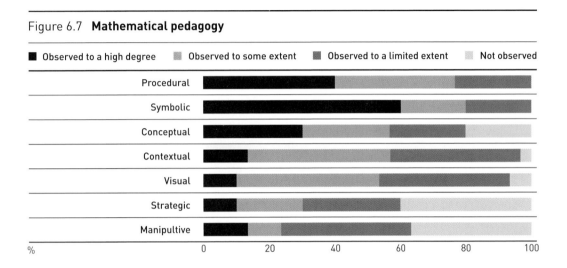

Overall

Figure 6.8 is a summary of all the 48 categories that were used to analyse teachers' pedagogical approaches, and it presents the average degree to which each was observed across all of the sessions observed.

Figure 6.8 **Mean ratings for each teaching characteristic in order of frequency**

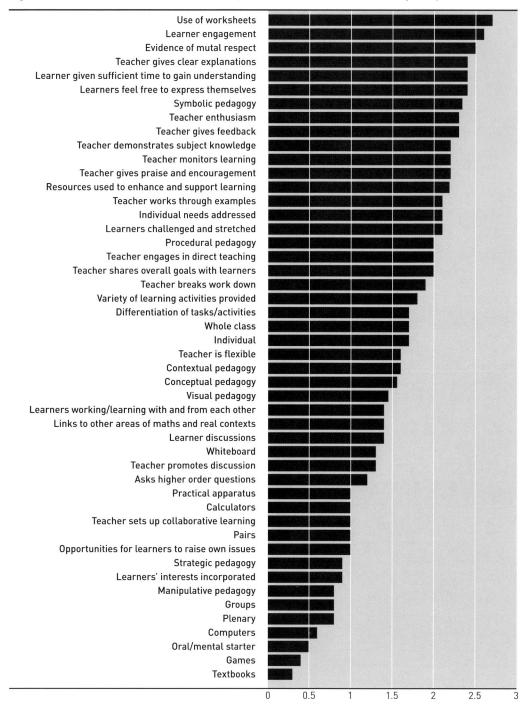

The table shows the most common form of organisation was whole-class and learners working individually. There was less group or collaborative work, and it was less typical to find learners working with, and learning from, each other.

Most teachers followed a set scheme of work and it was rare for them to incorporate learners' personal interests. The main pedagogical approach employed was for teachers to show learners procedures, breaking concepts down into smaller parts and demonstrating examples. Resources were generally used to enhance and support learning. The use of worksheets was widespread, and there was little use of practical apparatus, games or ICT.

Teachers generally had adequate subject knowledge, gave clear explanations and provided a variety of learning activities. It was less usual for teachers to differentiate work, make connections to other areas of mathematics, or ask higher-order questions to encourage higher-level thinking or to probe learners' blocks and misconceptions.

Mutual respect between teachers and learners was high, and learners felt free to express themselves. Teachers were invariably enthusiastic and gave learners lots of praise and encouragement. They also usually monitored learning and gave learners feedback.

On the whole, learners were generally highly engaged; they were often challenged and stretched; they were given time to gain understanding, and the majority had their individual needs met.

6.3 Teaching typologies and other factors

Based on the classroom observations, it was decided to classify teachers according to their teaching approach. Three approaches to teaching were identified: the *connectionist* and *transmission* styles (Askew et al., 1997), and the *constructivist/scaffolder* style, after Bruner and Vygotsky (see Wood, Bruner and Ross, 1976; Vygotsky, 1993). No teacher in the sample used a *discovery* approach to teaching, that is where, guided by the teacher and materials, the teacher believes that learners should discover the intended outcome of the lesson (Askew et al., 1997; Hammer, 1997). Distinguishing features of each approach are given below. It should be noted that we have adapted the definition of these styles to apply not to teachers' orientations, which they were originally used to describe in the work of Askew et al., but to observed behaviours. This is partly why we have found it necessary to add the category of *constructivist,* since there seemed to be two distinct teaching styles used by teachers who might all have been described by Askew et al. as connectionist in orientation.

- The *connectionist* teacher is concerned to develop the conceptual understanding of learners and frequently makes connections to other areas of mathematics, including moving between symbolic, visual and verbal representations.
- The *transmission* teacher is principally concerned with mastery of skills. Mathematics is seen as a series of discrete packages to be taught in small steps emphasising procedures rather than conceptual understanding.
- Using the *constructivist/scaffolder* style, the teacher works alongside learners, co-constructing concepts and asking questions. The teacher provides a series of activities to help raise learners' thinking and conceptual understanding to a higher level.

The teaching typologies described above should be seen as theoretical ideal types. Most teachers use combinations of the different approaches to varying extents. We are not attempting to make value judgments as to whether any one approach is preferable; indeed, each could be perceived as appropriate to different purposes in teaching mathematics.

We also decided to classify the teacher approaches on a continuum by looking at other factors such as whether it was *open* or *closed*. In open classes the teacher allowed learners to shape the content and pace of the lesson and would often start from where the learners were (learner-centred). In *closed* classes teachers retained control of the lesson, working to a fixed plan with a predetermined end point (teacher-centred).

Learner engagement in the lessons was also classified according to whether learners were observed to be *active* or *passive* participants. *Active* learners were visibly engaged on a task either individually or, more usually, in a pair or group. There was a buzz of involvement and learners were seen to be interacting with each other and the teacher. In contrast, *passive* learners were judged to be working in a perfunctory manner, seemingly going through the motions without being particularly involved with the task/activity. On occasions they might be sitting still, possibly listening to the teacher but not interacting with the teacher or with other learners.

Teaching typologies; whether the teaching was open or closed; and whether the learners were active or passive; were all scored using the four-point scale described in Section 6.2. The findings will be discussed in Chapter 7, and illustrated in Figure 7.4.

6.4 Summary

Teachers felt they needed to be well-prepared, knowledgeable and in particular flexible to cope with the diversity of learner attainment, attitude, preferred mode of learning and attendance patterns. Some thought that this diversity, together with the range of possible types of activity to meet different mathematical aims, meant that no one pattern of lesson activity or organisational method was optimum, even with a specific class.

The session observation revealed that whole-class and individual work predominated, with teachers demonstrating procedures and learners working through worksheets. There were few higher-order questions, little pair or group work, and little use of practical resources or ICT, although activities were varied. Learners were usually highly engaged and relations were good between teachers and learners, with teachers enthusiastic, generous in giving praise and clear in their explanations.

Teaching typologies were identified to try to describe differences between approaches.

7 Teaching and learning: correlations between practice and progress

This chapter looks at correlations between learners' progress in attainment and attitude, and observed classroom characteristics and teaching approaches. The chapter ends with an example illustrating effective practice.

In our analysis we make the distinction described in Chapter 6 between *classroom characteristics* and *teaching approaches*, although they are inextricably linked. *Classroom characteristics* are based on the classroom sessions we observed and include both the features of the teachers' and the learners' activity. *Teaching approaches* relates to teachers' pedagogy, which is likely to be based on their perceived role and beliefs about teaching, learning and the nature of mathematics. This includes the degree to which the pedagogy is 'open' or 'closed', and the learners 'active' or 'passive'.

7.1 Correlations between class characteristics, progress and attitude

We computed correlations between the average scores for each of the classroom characteristics observed and the class gains. Most of the correlations were relatively low and not significant, whether or not we controlled for the effect of the phase when the observations occurred. Since the gains were larger in Phase 2, and there were minor changes in the observation instrument with more observations made per class, we have used only the Phase 2 data with 29 classes for the next section.

One significant *positive* correlation was found. This was between learners' progress and the extent to which procedural teaching was taking place (Spearman's *rho* = 0.45, *p* = 0.01). Figure 7.1 shows a scatterplot that illustrates these relationships with the extent to which the characteristic was observed in each class on the x-axis and the assessment gain for each class on the y-axis.

Figure 7.1 **Scatterplot of amount of procedural teaching and mean gain in assessment scores** (Note: the amount of procedural teaching was rated on a 0–3 scale with 0 = 'not observed', 1 = 'observed to a very limited extent', 2 = 'observed to some extent', 3 = 'observed to a high degree', and is averaged across observations of a class)

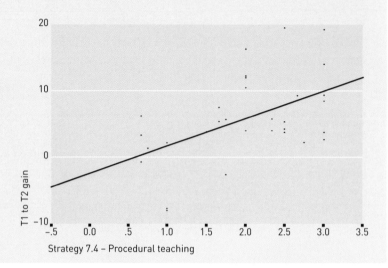

Procedural teaching involves teaching showing discrete procedures for learners to follow in order to carry out a computation or technique. As Figure 7.1 illustrates, classes where procedural teaching was observed to a very limited extent (values below 1.5 on the scatterplot) tended to make less progress than those where procedural teaching was emphasised more. However, there was no clear difference in the progress made by classes where procedural teaching was observed to either some extent or to a high degree (between 2 and 3 on the scatterplot).

It is not immediately clear why those classes where lower degrees of procedural teaching were observed performed less well. It could be that teachers were concerned to support learners who had difficulty with retaining procedures, and were thus more inclined to emphasise more conceptual aspects with learners who made less progress. The assessment instrument did include procedural knowledge but there did not seem to be an over-emphasis on this.

Two significant but low *negative* correlations were found. These were between learner progress and the amount of individual work taking place, and the extent to which appropriate resources were used to support and enhance learning (*rho* = –0.34, *p* = 0.02 and *rho* = –0.32, *p* = 0.03 respectively). In other words, classes in which these characteristics were observed less were more likely to have made positive gains (Figures 7.2 and 7.3).

Figure 7.2 **Scatterplot of the amount of individual work** (rated on a 0–3 scale) and mean class gain in assessment scores

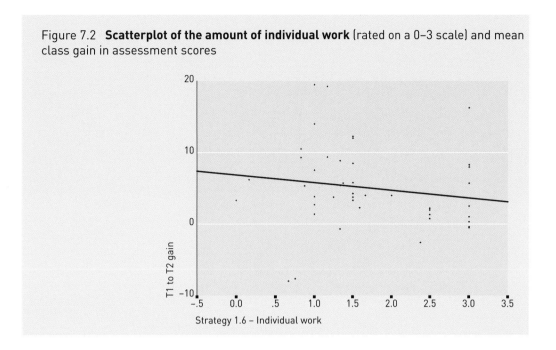

As can be seen from Figure 7.2, almost every class contained individual work at least to a limited extent, and the relationship is not strong; indeed, one of the classes that made the best progress contained a significant amount of individual work. However, classes in which individual work was observed to a large extent (above 2.5 on the graph) generally seemed to make a little less progress.

During the study, we observed some classes in which the teacher relied almost entirely on individual work, generally based on worksheets and portfolios. One disadvantage of classes where individualised work predominated was that the teacher was sometimes in high demand, and could spend only a limited amount of time with each learner. However, once again, there are circumstances that dictate that learners work in this way: in work-based learning, individual learners might start and leave at different times, and some classes had only one or two learners. As we reported in Section 6.1, some teachers also said that some learners preferred to work this way.

The weak but significant negative correlation found between the extent to which appropriate resources were used to enhance and support learning and learner progress is more difficult to explain. First, though, the term use of resources to 'support and enhance learning' is a value judgement and different researchers may have had different interpretations, and second, in the analysis we were unable to identify the combination of resources being used.

Figure 7.3 **Scatterplot of the amount of resources used to support and enhance learning** (rated on a 0–3 scale) and mean class gain in assessment scores

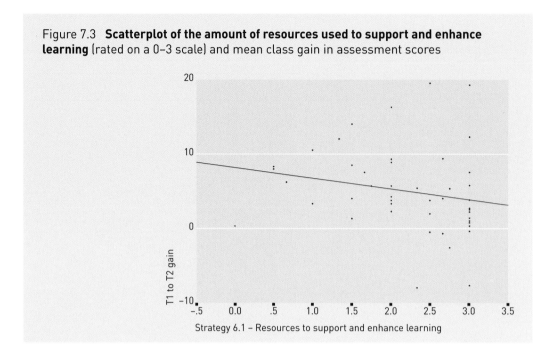

Strategy 6.1 – Resources to support and enhance learning

The correlation could be the result of a confounding variable, i.e. a negative characteristic of the class affects learners' progress and cancels out any positive effect from the use of resources. In this case there might well be a tendency for more resources to be used in classes where learners had the most difficulty in learning numeracy. Note that the use of resources is not strongly related to gains.

7.2 Correlations between teaching approaches and gains in progress and attitude

The results are shown in Figure 7.4. Within this triangle, each dot represents a class. The position of the dot indicates the teaching typology, which is a balance between transmission, connectionist and constructivist methods. The closer the dot is to one of the angles, the more important this method was judged to be within the teaching typology. The shade/pattern of the dot represents the progress the class made: black-dot classes made negative progress, white-dot classes made poor but positive progress, grey-dot classes made reasonable progress, and striped-dot classes made good or very good progress. As can be seen, there is no perceptible pattern within this triangle. This indicates that there is no clear relationship between teaching typology and class progress.

Figure 7.4 **Pattern between teacher typology and class gains**

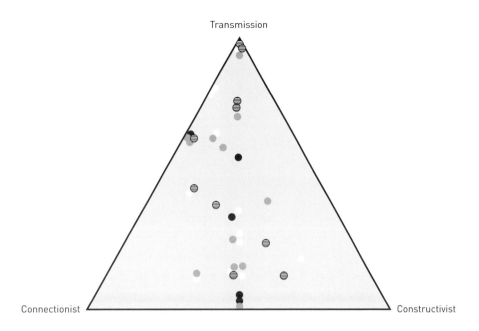

We also found no significant correlations either between any of these three factors, or between teaching typologies and changes in learners' attitudes.

This lack of success in finding significant correlations between teaching typologies and either gains in attainment or in attitude again seems surprising. However, such findings are not unusual in the mathematics education literature, where it is first the learner variables and second the curriculum followed which seemed to be the essential factors; the effect of the manner in which the teaching takes place is either not detected or is very small (Burstein, 1992; Galton, 1989). Mortimore et al. (1988), in a large-scale study of primary attainment in London, estimate the effect of the teacher as accounting for less than 10 per cent of the variance left *after the very much stronger effects of differences in pupil variables have been taken into account*. Our study, having a much smaller sample of learners and instruments which are probably less sensitive, was not able to measure at this level of discrimination.

It thus seems likely that in our study too, factors which cannot easily be determined in a large-scale survey may have more influence on their learning and changes in attitudes than any specific easily-observed difference in teacher behaviour. These factors include learners' strength of motivation, self-discipline, aspirations, abilities and dispositions towards numeracy, socio-cultural background and previous experiences both inside and outside the classroom.

7.3 Analysis of features of practice in classes where learners made the greatest progress

We went on to examine the highest performing classes, in the sense of those that made greatest gains, in greater depth to find out whether any particular features distinguished the teaching of these classes from the others. We selected the five classes that made the most progress, all achieving mean gains of more than 15 per cent. We then compared these five classes with the full sample in several different ways, as described below. We also looked for differences in the teachers' background characteristics.

There was a considerable variety of teaching typologies even within these five classes. Two teachers were judged to use a connectionist/constructivist approach, one a connectionist/ transmission approach and two a transmission approach. While the teachers in the two best performing classes (both of which achieved more than 30 per cent attainment gains) predominantly used a balance of constructivist and connectionist approaches, other classes taught using similar approaches performed much less well. A typical example of a connectionist/constructivist lesson with one of these two highest performing classes is given in Section 7.4.

When we came to look at the other teaching approaches, we found that the learners in four of the classes were relatively active (that is they were classified as scoring 2 or 3 on the four-point scale 0–3 already described), and the teaching tended to be closed, with only one teacher scoring 3 for an open teaching style. There were no clear associations with either the way the classes were organised (in terms of whole-class, individual or group teaching), or with the teachers' levels of experience and qualifications.

We also examined the classroom characteristics within the five classes to find whether they differed from those observed in the sample as a whole. Using the quantitative data from classroom observations, we calculated the effect size for each characteristic. This measures the size of the difference between the average extent to which that characteristic was observed in the five top-performing classes and that for the sample as a whole. The higher the effect size (either positive or negative), the more pronounced is the difference between these five classes and the rest of the sample. Table 7.1 shows the characteristics that had effect sizes higher than 0.5. The positive effect sizes were factors which occurred to a greater extent in the five top-performing classes, while the negative ones are those which occurred to a lesser extent than in the sample as a whole.

We went on to run significance tests (t-tests) for each of these characteristics; the characteristics shown in bold in Table 7.1 are those for which there is a significant difference in extent ($p < 0.05$) between the five top-performing classes and the average.

Table 7.1 **Characteristics with effect sizes >0.5 i.e those which best distinguish the five highest performing classes from the average (bolded characteristics also significant at p<0.05)**

Characteristics observed to a greater(+) or lesser(-) extent in the top 5 classes	Effect size
Whole class teaching	**+1.06**
Learners linking work to previous knowledge	+0.93
Use of whiteboard	**+0.90**
Use of interactive board	**+0.88**
Use of plenary session	**+0.87**
Teacher engages in direct teaching	**+0.82**
Teacher sets up practical activities	**-0.78**
Teacher links maths to previous work	**+0.76**
Teacher works through examples	+0.75
Teacher shares overall goals with learners	+0.75
Mathematical pedagogy: procedural	**+0.72**
Mathematical pedagogy: symbolic	+0.67
Learners learn with and from each other	+0.65
Individualised work	-0.65
Learners disrupt the session	-0.64
Teacher sets up written activities	+0.63
Learners copy from board	+0.58
Mathematical pedagogy: manipulative	-0.58
Use of practical apparatus	-0.57
Pair work	+0.56
Learners feel free to express themselves	+0.55
Teacher links work to real life	+0.55
Mathematical pedagogy: conceptual	+0.52

It can be seen from Table 7.1 that the classroom characteristics which have a large positive effect size and are significant in distinguishing the five groups with the highest gains from the average for all groups were mainly associated with traditional front-of-class teaching of mathematical procedures, including a final 'plenary' session to summarise the lesson.

We went on to check which characteristics also had effect sizes over 0.5 in the five lowest-performing classes as compared with the average, and at the differences between these two extreme sets.

Some characteristics occurred more frequently than average in both the highest and lowest performing groups and thus did not differentiate between them. These characteristics were the extent of:

■ whole-class teaching (effect sizes of +1.06 and +0.60 respectively for highest and lowest performing groups)
■ use of whiteboard (effect sizes of +0.90 and +0.71)
■ learners learn with and from each other (+0.65 and +0.80).

No characteristics appeared less frequently in both groups when compared with the average.

The fact that greater proportions of whole-class teaching are associated with both highest and lowest gains was also found in the primary numeracy studies carried out by the Leverhulme Numeracy Research Project (Brown et al., 2001).

However, there were two characteristics where the effect sizes for the highest and lowest performing groups appeared with opposite signs in the two lists, thus showing that they not only differentiated each group from the average but very clearly differentiated between these groups from each other. These were:

- teacher sets up practical activities (–0.78 and +1.74 respectively for the highest performing and lowest performing groups)
- mathematics pedagogy: procedural (+0.72 and –0.99).

Thus the teachers of the five groups that made the highest gains generally taught mathematical procedures more than the average teacher, and very much more than the teachers of the five groups which gained least. This is consistent with procedural teaching having the highest correlation with gains for the whole sample, reported in Section 7.1. Similarly, teachers of the five groups that made the highest gains made less use of practical activities than the average teacher and very much less use than teachers of the five groups who made the least gains. While not completely consistent with the correlation evidence, there is obviously a strong association between this observation and the only characteristic which was negatively correlated with gains, which was 'appropriate resources are used to enhance and support learning'.

As we noted in Section 7.1, it is important to guard against converting distinctions into causations. In this case it seems likely that teachers decide to use practical equipment for learners who have difficulties in learning; in almost all such classrooms we observed, we felt this use was appropriate.

Similarly, teachers would be unlikely to try to teach formal procedures to learners who had experienced problems in remembering these in the past; it would be more likely that they would do so for faster learners. We do not therefore believe that the conclusion should be drawn that procedural teaching causes greater learning and practical activities cause lesser learning.

Other aspects of what would normally be regarded as effective practice were used more among the lowest-performing classes, e.g. collaborative work, teaching of strategies as well as procedures, teachers emphasising making connections and hypotheses. Again, we do not believe that these are counter-productive; indeed, we found classes where researchers with many years of experience in education thought that the teaching was generally very good but learner progress was weak. Equally, we observed some teaching we felt was of lower than average quality but where progress was strong.

Finally, we also checked to see if the characteristics of the learners might have an effect. The five highest attaining classes all contained adults over 19 and tended to be dominated by older learners without any major language difficulties, which further supports the results in Section 5.3. No other clear associations were found.

7.4 An example of effective practice

The aim of this section is to present a detailed description of one teacher's numeracy class as an example of effective practice. We also believe that readers need to see what a numeracy class looks like from the inside.

The class took place in an FE college in London, and ran for two hours on one evening each week. It consisted of about 14 learners working at Entry level 3 to Level 1, and the age range was 18 to 60-plus. The teacher was an experienced numeracy tutor; she has a PGCE in secondary education; her highest maths qualification is at A-level; and, at the time of the observation, she had been teaching numeracy for 21 years.

In terms of assessment results, this class achieved an average gain of more than 30 per cent, with many learners making exceptional progress. In addition, learners' enthusiasm towards numeracy was noticeable both from the attitude surveys and the class observations. This was achieved by using a predominantly connectionist and constructivist approach which emphasised conceptual understanding rather than routine procedures. Mathematics learning was conceived as participating in a network where the teachers and learners construct concepts together.

The teacher created a non-threatening atmosphere and learners' misconceptions were used as examples to discuss with the whole group. Learners were encouraged to discuss problems and concepts both between themselves and with the teacher, building a strong collaborative culture. Numeracy learning was viewed as social activity in which people took ownership of what they were doing, and where understanding was formed through discussion. A variety of group, individual and whole-class teaching was used; however, even when learning was organised on an individual basis the learners were still encouraged to discuss problems and help each other, developing a greater understanding. The class was taught in an open style, which allowed higher-order, diagnostic questioning that uncovered learners' thinking.

A range of materials and teaching resources was used, from worksheets to games and activities including whole-class role-play. Calculators were freely available. The teacher used problem-solving activities which challenged the learners. She was also flexible and able to change direction to respond to the learners' needs.

Figure 7.5 is an extract from a researcher's observation sheet. It is a narrative account that was filled in contemporaneously, and attempts to describe what was going on. Of course it only provides a partial snapshot, and for the purposes of this example, and in the interests of space, we are only using the first hour of the session. The comments that appear in italics are retrospective and were not included on the original sheet; they are not intended to be exhaustive, but provide characteristics of what we believe constitute effective practice. The narrative also shows how complex teaching is; how many decisions teachers have to make; and how hard they often have to work. The names of the teacher and learners have been changed.

Figure 7.5 **A narrative account of a numeracy session from a researcher's observations sheet**

Time	Content/focus of the session

7.00 | **Topic: Percentages**

Becky (BH) holds up an individual mini-whiteboard (A4 white laminated card) with '%' hand-drawn on it. She asks the learners to tell her what it is and what it means. In response to one learner saying it looked like a division sign, she draws a division sign [÷] on the main (fixed) whiteboard and initiates a discussion about the relationship between percentages, fractions and decimals.

She asks learners to call out different percentages that they had come across, and she writes them up on the main whiteboard . BH writes up: '10% means divide by 10'. She makes no further comment.

The teacher asks open questions; does not give answers; initiates discussion, looks at relationships and connections and assesses learners' prior knowledge. The teaching is interactive and the teacher reinforces understanding.

7.15 | BH gives learners small cards with statements on two lines (e.g., I have 76. Who has 10 per cent of £6,500?) Learners have to read out their questions and answer if they have the right answer, otherwise keep quiet. BH: 'If your neighbour is quiet they may be asleep, so you can look at your neighbour's card.' At the end Becky confirms to the class that they were all able to calculate 10 per cent of the amount.

BH (having drawn on small whiteboard): '10 per cent of 30? So what's 5 per cent? So what's 30 per cent? If I wanted 90 per cent of 500?' Greg says, 'Take off 10 per cent'. BH asks for a number and Greg says '300': '50 per cent of 300? What's 75 per cent of 300? Half is 50 per cent, then halve that and add it to the 150. Notice we're talking about a half and a quarter.' Learners call out the answers; Becky writes on large whiteboard. BH: 'Can you see a pattern? What's 55 per cent of 300? You can do it however you like.' Learners hold up their whiteboard cards as they do it. They ask each other what they've got. Becky helps one man (Moji). She asks (re 55 per cent of 300) 'What would be an easy percentage?' Moji: '50 per cent'. BH: 'Sandra, tell Moji what to do' (she does). 'One way is to use what you know here and here' (shows examples on main whiteboard).

BH points out there are many different ways of doing percentages. In some situations one method is good, in others, another method might be better. '$17\frac{1}{2}$ per cent. If you think you know what to do, write it down on your board. 10 per cent; 5 per cent; $2\frac{1}{2}$ per cent. What have they done here? Can you work out $17\frac{1}{2}$ per cent of 300?' (shows it written on mini whiteboard with figures above each other). Learners work out each element and then add them together. BH asks why they've added them. Learners explain. BH: 'That's VAT. It's not too bad. Now try it with my nice number (400). Just to see how comfortable you are with it, I'll give you an even nicer number (800).' Sandra gives the right answer. BH: 'Did you do that in your head? That's impressive. So $17\frac{1}{2}$ per cent doesn't hold any threats for you. How about 63 per cent? How will I break that down?' (Learners call out different ways of breaking down 63 per cent). BH: 'Distinguish between ones you can do in your head and more tricky ones – you'd use a calculator for those.'

BH: 'Let's try 63 per cent of £800.' She goes around the room (using the space in the middle) helping learners as appropriate, e.g., not lining numbers up. BH: 'There's a terribly dangerous thing happening to everyone in the room and it's all my fault! Karen, let me show what you did.' She writes 400 wrongly aligned with the other numbers to be added. BH: 'Be careful that you always find percentages of the same number (800). Always refer back to the number you're finding the percentage of.' BH: 'Will 63 per cent be more than half or less than half? Always think about doing a check. There are different ways of checking. We can learn some of those as we go along.' BH: (writing on whiteboard): 'When you see 25 per cent what does it mean? A quarter; 75 per cent, three-quarters; $33\frac{1}{3}$, a third.'

The teacher uses interactive games and asks questions. She builds on, and uses, learners' strategies, points out that there are many different strategies that can be used, highlights that some may be better than others, and shows learners which ones to use. The teacher is, again, getting learners to look for patterns. The learners work collaboratively; some assume a teaching role and explain strategies to each other. The teacher breaks maths down and works through examples. She points out that there are different ways of solving problems. The teacher assesses different ways of working and asks learners to justify what they've done. She breaks maths down using learners' own methods, and encourages mental calculation. She gives praise and there is appropriate use of technology. The teacher monitors learning and identifies learners' misconceptions. She emphasises need for checking and reinforces concepts learned with whole group.

7.5 Summary

It has proved very difficult to find many clear associations between either teaching approaches or classroom characteristics and changes in learning or attitudes. The only significant positive correlation with learning gains was with the extent of procedural teaching. This also comes out as a factor differentiating the group of classes who make the highest gains with those making the lowest gains. There is also some evidence that the teachers of the highest gaining group tend to use to a greater extent than average other aspects of traditional teaching such as teaching directly to the whole class, and a whiteboard (both interactive or traditional). However, whole-class teaching and the use of a static whiteboard were also more prevalent in the classes with the lowest gains.

The only significant negative correlations with attainment gains were with the 'appropriate use of resources to enhance and support learning' and with the extent of individual work. Contrasting the groups which made the highest gains with those making the lowest gains, use of practical activities also appeared to be much more closely associated with the lower performing groups.

These characteristics, however, cannot necessarily be claimed to be a cause of effective, or ineffective, teaching; it seems likely that they are more an indication that teachers change their style of teaching when faced with learners who are experiencing great difficulties in learning, and adopt a more practical and less formal approach.

Equally, there is considerable variety in teaching typologies and classroom characteristics among both the highest and lowest performing classes. An example is given of part of a lesson with one of the two highest attaining classes. Although this style of teaching is by definition effective and would meet current perceptions of good practice, it does not exemplify those characteristics which correlate best with high average gains and it includes some features which correlate with low gains.

8 Distinctive aspects of the numeracy project

This chapter is divided into two sections: the first considers distinctive factors in adult numeracy teaching; the second looks at the distinctive aspects of this study.

8.1 What is distinctive about adult numeracy teaching?

Adult numeracy teaching is particularly complex for several reasons. First, numeracy is not a discrete skill or set of skills: it is intimately bound up with literacy and language. Numeracy problems may be presented through texts involving written words, numbers and symbols or through spoken language; writing may also be required. This causes difficulties for learners with weaknesses in these areas (and a challenge for us in the administration of our assessment instrument and attitude survey). Second, numeracy is not a discrete skill in another sense: adults' numerate practices are deeply embedded in the contexts in which they occur (Coben et al., 2003). Learners may or may not recognise the mathematics involved in different activities and contexts. Moreover, transfer of learning between these may be problematic (Carraher et al. 1985; Lave 1988), posing a challenge for teachers attempting to relate the curriculum to learners' lives and, in embedded provision, to the subject area for which numeracy is required. Third, numeracy skills are 'more fluid, less ingrained' than literacy skills (Parsons et al. 2005), which implies that levels of achievement may not be stable across time or under varying circumstances. Fourth, adult numeracy education is exceptionally diverse. Finally, we know that some adults have strong negative feelings and/or anxiety about mathematics, amounting in some cases to 'mathophobia' (Winter, 1992).

8.2 What is distinctive about this study?

Two issues proved particularly problematic in this study: encompassing the diversity of adult numeracy provision and teaching and measuring learners' progress.

The effect of the diversity of adult numeracy education on the study

As we noted in Section 2.3, adult numeracy education takes various forms, occurs in various contexts, and has a wide range of teachers and learners. It is extremely heterogeneous by comparison, not only with numeracy and mathematics education in schools, but also with other *Skills for Life* areas. These factors make it difficult to produce generic research instruments able to encompass the full range of learners, teachers and forms of provision, or to draw conclusions that can be generalised across the whole sector. This difficulty was particularly acute in measuring learners' progress.

Issues in the measurement of learners' progress

Learners' progress against an assessment instrument (standardised test) is treated as a mark of effective teaching and learning in this study, as in the study on which these projects are based (Condelli, 2001) and in the other NRDC Effective Practice Studies. We were aware at the outset that there is a lack of adult-friendly, linguistically- and culturally-sensitive instruments for assessing numeracy (Brooks et al. 2005), and that 'the measurement of adult numeracy skills is problematic, especially for adults with lower ability levels (including special educational needs and dyscalculia) and/or reading or language difficulties' (Coben, et al. 2003: 1).

We reviewed several instruments against criteria established in an international review of assessment procedures in adult numeracy[10] (Cumming and Gal, 2000) and our wider knowledge of the research literature before deciding on that used in the *Skills for Life* national survey of need in adult literacy and numeracy (DfES, 2003b). This we modified as the result of our experience of using it in our trial phase and in Phase 1 of the study.

However, the modified assessment instrument still did not meet all our requirements. It was weak in terms of reliability at *Skills for Life* levels and insufficiently sensitive with respect to the diverse range of learners in the study. It particularly lacked validity with learners at or below Entry level 1, those with learning difficulties and disabilities, and learners whose reading or command of the English language was poor.

The need for our assessment instrument to be practicable – not take up too much class time – was also problematic. There was an inevitable trade-off between getting more information and taking up too much of the learners' time in class. Considerations of practicality, as well as the absence of available assessment instruments in a range of formats, also meant that we could not 'encompass the range of assessment forms being used in other educational settings and may include oral reports, group activities, portfolios, and so forth'. We were aware that 'adult learners may perform at quite different levels in oral mathematical discussions than on written tasks' (Cumming and Gal, 2000) but for reasons of practicality and reliability (consistency) we used a written test. Another limitation of our chosen assessment instrument – perhaps any numeracy assessment instrument – is also pertinent here: the areas of mathematics taught in class may not have matched those covered in the assessment. Some areas may have already been known to learners, or been learned independently, outside the class. Some learners may have been tested on areas of mathematics that were not taught in the period between our assessments. Either way, we cannot be certain that correct or incorrect answers result from teaching in the class.

Factors outlined in Section 8.1, above, may also have a negative impact on learners' performance in tests. For example, poor readers, or those with a weak grasp of English may not be able to read or understand words or notation used in the assessment or be unfamiliar with the visual clues given; anxiety or poor memory may impede the performance of some learners. There is also a wider issue of the difficulty (some would say, impossibility) of simulating in the classroom situations in which mathematics occurs elsewhere (Dowling, 1991). Hence an assessment might not give a clear indication of an individual's strengths and weaknesses when confronted with mathematics outside the classroom. For all these reasons, the assessment of numeracy is especially complex and further research is needed to produce robust assessment instruments able to encompass all the factors outlined above.

---

10 Albeit for class teaching purposes, rather than for measuring progress in research studies such as ours.

9 Conclusions

A summary of the main conclusions of the study can be found in in Chapter 1.

9.1 Reflections

In one sense our findings mirror research literature that suggests that there is often only a partial relationship between interactions in pedagogic settings and learning. A common theme in our study is the complexity of the process of adult numeracy teaching and learning, and we agree with Ivanič and Tseng (2005), who caution against any attempt to promote a single method or approach across all settings. However, while learning can rarely be reduced to the sum of what has been taught in a classroom, this does not negate the attempt to continue seeking generalisations about relationships between specific teaching approaches, classroom characteristics and learning outcomes.

We have found, though, that effective approaches are difficult to determine from quantitative data alone. The multiplicity of factors contributing to learning means that any effects that effective practice might have are often compromised by other considerations that contribute to, or constrain, learner progress. In the end, our correlation calculations give little indication of what constitutes an effective approach in adult numeracy education. The data do suggest some classroom characteristics that are *consistently associated with the classes that made most progress* and this may have some implications for effective teaching practice. However, we cannot be certain that these characteristics (which were restricted in number and implemented within very different teaching approaches) were, either individually or overall, the *cause* of learners' progress. Many factors may determine the effectiveness of a teaching programme.

It might simplistically be thought that there is a direct relationship between quality of teaching and quality of learning, such that the better the teaching, the greater the rises in attainment over time. This was demonstrably not so; we found classes where researchers with many years of experience of observing classrooms thought that the teaching was good, but learner progress was weak, and some apparently poor teaching of classes where the gains turned out to be relatively large. This suggests that factors which cannot easily be determined in a large-scale survey may have more influence on their learning than any specific easily-observed difference in teacher behaviour. These factors include learners' strength of motivation, self-discipline, aspirations, abilities and dispositions towards numeracy, socio-cultural background and previous experiences both inside and outside the classroom.

9.2 Implications and recommendations for practice, teacher education and CPD, policy and research

Practice

While we are unable, on the basis of our correlation data, to firmly recommend any particular teaching practice or set of practices, we believe that we saw some effective practice in our study. For example, the glimpse of one teacher's practice given in Section 7.4, we believe, exemplifies some of the key features of effective practice. These resonate with the approaches promoted by the DfES Standards Unit *Improving Learning in Mathematics* project that are currently being piloted with adult learners at Entry level and Level 1 through the NRDC Maths4Life *Thinking Through Mathematics* project (www.maths4life.org.uk). This belief is based on our combined experience and expertise, supported, to a very limited extent, by our data. For example, some learners made much less progress with teachers who used similar approaches, in classes with similar characteristics.

We also suspect that the characteristics of the learners and how they position themselves as learners in relation to the subject matter, the teacher and other learners might be important. We therefore used qualitative methods to supplement our quantitative data, interviewing learners and teachers. Findings from these interviews are presented in Chapter 4 and Section 6.1. They bear out the view that it is the flexibility of teachers in deploying well-grounded mathematical pedagogy, while adapting their teaching to the diversity of adult numeracy learners and organisational contexts, that seems to be key to effective practice.

There were some instances of poor classroom management and, in a very few cases, teachers appeared to have inadequate subject knowledge. For example, one teacher gave a muddled and incorrect explanation of the difference between discrete and continuous data, and another had difficulty converting centilitres to millilitres. Interestingly, the first teacher holds a good degree in mathematics. There is an assumption that individuals holding high qualifications in mathematics will automatically be able to teach basic concepts at lower levels of mathematics. We argue that this is not necessarily the case, and that some teachers relied substantially on methods they had been taught at school. The implications of this for teacher education and CPD are discussed in the next section.

Teacher education and CPD

On the basis of our study, we believe that considerable improvements are needed in training specialist numeracy teachers and in the quality of numeracy teaching if greater progress is to be made towards producing flexible, expert teachers and successful learners. There is a general lack of training opportunities and CPD in adult numeracy, compounded by a shortage of qualified and experienced numeracy specialists able to teach the new Level 4 training courses (Lucas et al, 2004).

Many teachers in our study were generally well qualified to teach at *Skills for Life* levels, given that the new Level 4 courses were in their first year of operation in Phase 1 of the study. As noted in Section 3.1, 79 per cent reported having a formal qualification in mathematics or a related subject (e.g., science); 88 per cent reported having a teaching qualification; and 18 per cent reported having a Level 4 Certificate for adult numeracy subject specialists. However, some teachers lacked sufficient grounding, and had not been trained in teaching basic mathematical concepts. These teachers did not have the 'profound understanding of fundamental mathematics' that Liping Ma, in her research with US and Chinese secondary mathematics teachers, regards as essential (Ma, 1999). This should not surprise us, since there is no requirement in the current Subject Specifications for Adult Numeracy for teachers to have a firm understanding of basic concepts of, say, place value or multiplication or division. Also, generic courses for teachers in the Learning and Skills sector (e.g., Cert Ed. or PGCE) currently deal only with general, rather than subject-specific, pedagogy. We believe teachers need guidance on subject-specific (in this case, mathematical) pedagogy so that they not only have in-depth subject knowledge, but also are able to provide learners with a rich variety of learning activities geared to their level of experience and area of interest. Research by the NRDC (Lucas et al, 2004) has identified the omission of subject specialist pedagogy as a significant weakness in the current FENTO (now LLUK) Subject Specifications for Teachers of Adult Literacy, Numeracy and ESOL originally published in 2002 (DfES/FENTO, 2002). We think we have seen the outcome of this omission in some of the classrooms we have observed and we recommend that the gap should be filled. We are heartened to note that draft revised subject specifications for adult numeracy published for consultation by LLUK in February 2006 include a section on 'Knowledge and Understanding of Area of Teaching Application' (http://www.lifelonglearninguk.org/currentactivity/newdevelopments/rev_subj_specs.html). We also recommend the establishment of specialist PGCE (FE) courses in mathematics, including numeracy.

Policy

The implications for policy in our study with respect to teaching and teacher education and professional development are set out in the preceding sections in this chapter. Beyond these key areas, we make the following observations and recommendations. The diversity and complexity of adult numeracy education are facts of life to which policy must accommodate because they reflect the diversity of adult learners and their purposes in studying numeracy.

Mathematics and numeracy suffer from a curious invisibility in that people often do not recognise when they are successfully using mathematics – being numerate – either in class or in their lives beyond the classroom. We agree with the comment by Celia Hoyles, Chief Adviser for Mathematics at the DfES, that 'The invisibility of maths is pervasive – and something we have to struggle with at all levels' (www.nrdc.org.uk/content.asp?CategoryID=592&ArticleID=485).

For too long, numeracy has been, if not quite invisible, at least obscured by being subsumed within adult literacy in policy documents at all levels, including inspection reports.

Adult numeracy education should be seen as part of mathematics education as well as in relation to adult literacy and the other *Skills for Life* areas. This should be reflected in the organisation and inspection of provision, so that, for example, adult numeracy provision is effectively co-ordinated with other mathematics provision offered by colleges and other organisations, thereby maximising learners' opportunities for progression. We welcome the inclusion of adult numeracy education in the work of the new National Centre for Excellence in the Teaching of Mathematics (NCETM) and trust that the new Regional Centres for Mathematics will support the development of effective practice across the whole range of mathematics and numeracy education.

Finally, numeracy is invisible in another way. There is a dearth of information about adult numeracy and mathematics provision in the Learning and Skills sector, as we found when we tried to target our advertisements for teachers and sites for our study. Data should be routinely collected and accessible to researchers and other professionals and the general public. In the meantime, we welcome the fact that Maths4Life is conducting an initial workforce study to establish the range of information that is currently available and identify gaps.

We also welcome, in principle, the imminent introduction of Functional Mathematics, in which:

Each individual has sufficient understanding of a range of mathematical concepts and is able to know how and when to use them. For example, they will have the confidence and capability to use maths to solve problems embedded in increasingly complex settings and to use a range of tools, including ICT, as appropriate.

In life and work, each individual will develop the analytical and reasoning skills to draw conclusions, justify how they are reached and to identify errors or inconsistencies. They will also be able to validate and interpret results, to judge the limits of their validity and use them effectively and efficiently. (QCA, 2005:2)

We see this as essential if the more ambitious targets for skills development needed to establish a world-class skills base in the UK by 2020 envisaged in the Leitch Review of skills are to be achieved (Leitch, 2005).

Research

One of the difficulties of this study was the heterogeneity of both the contexts and the learners. If it was decided to pursue further the possibility of a correlational study to identify effective practice, we would suggest that it needs to be carried out within much narrower limits to enable control of many of the factors other than teaching approaches. However, a major difficulty would be that the results would also be valid only within that narrow range and could not be readily generalised.

A much narrower range of learner initial attainment would also enable the design and use of an instrument which would be more sensitive to small changes in learners' progress. We recommend that further research and development are undertaken into learner assessment in numeracy at *Skills for Life* levels with a view to developing an appropriate assessment instrument for research purposes.

Alternatively, we believe that a project could be designed to test out some of the hypotheses from this study. This would identify teachers using a specific approach and use carefully selected matched control classes to compare rates of progress.

In focusing on a specific group we would suggest attention be given to the neediest learners, those at Entry level, whom we feel have been neglected in terms of research and development and for whom numeracy holds the key to improving their employment situation (Machin et al, 2001). Research could, for example, look at what kind of curriculum such learners would value and need for practical purposes.

We also feel that given the importance which emerged from the interviews of learners' motivations, there would be some advantage in exploring this in more depth. More generally, there is more scope for research to explore learner and teacher identities. Learners' identities are key because they affect attitudes, motivations, dispositions towards mathematics and the education system in general, relations with peers and teachers, and future expectations and aspirations. Teacher identities are also important and we need to find out how much personal investment teachers make both as numeracy teachers (as opposed to teachers of other subjects) and as mathematicians.

References

ALI/OFSTED (2001). The Common Inspection Framework for Inspecting Post-16 Education and Training. From http://www.ofsted.gov.uk/public/docs01/cif.pdf.

ALI/OFSTED (2003). *Literacy, Numeracy and English for Speakers of Other Languages: A review of current practice in post-16 and adult provision*. Coventry: Adult Learning Inspectorate, OFSTED and Her Majesty's Inspectorate.

Askew, M., Brown, M. et al. (1997). *Effective Teachers of Numeracy*. London: King's College London.

Barton, D. and Pitt, K. (2003). *Adult ESOL Pedagogy: A review of research, an annotated bibliography and recommendations for further research*. London: National Research and Development Centre for Adult Literacy and Numeracy (NRDC).

BERA (2004). *British Educational Research Association (BERA) Ethical Guidelines*. Revised 2004. Southwell.

Besser, S., Brooks, G., Burton, M., Parisella, M., Spare, Y., Stratford, S., and Wainright, J. (2004). *Adult Literacy Learners' Difficulties in Reading: An exploratory study*. London, National Research and Development Centre for Adult Literacy and Numeracy (NRDC).

Brooks, G., Giles, K., Harman, J., Kendal, S., Rees, F., and Whittaker, S. (2001). *Assembling the Fragments: A review of research on adult basic skills*. Research Report. Nottingham: Department for Education and Employment.

Brooks, G., Heath, K., and Pollard, A., (2005). *Assessing Adult Literacy and Numeracy: A review of assessment instruments*. London: National Research and Development Centre for Adult Literacy and Numeracy (NRDC).

Brown, M., Askew, M., Rhodes, V., Denvir, H., Ranson, E. and Wiliam, D. (2001) 'Magic bullets or chimeras? Searching for factors characterising effective teacher and effective teaching in numeracy.' Paper presented at the British Educational Research Conference, University of Leeds, September, 2001.

Burstein, L. (1992) *The IEA Study of Mathematics III: student growth and classroom processes*. Oxford: Pergamon Press.

Bynner, J. and Parsons, S., (1998). *Use it or Lose it? The impact of time out of work on literacy and numeracy skills*. London, Basic Skills Agency.

Carraher, T. N., Carraher, D. W., et al. (1985). Mathematics in the streets and in schools. *British Journal of Developmental Psychology* **3**: 21–29.

Coben, D. (2003). *Adult Numeracy: Review of research and related literature*. London: National Research and Development Centre for Adult Literacy and Numeracy (NRDC).

Condelli, L. (2001). *Effective Instruction for Adult ESL Literacy Students: Findings from the What Works study.* Washington, DC: American Institutes for Research.

Condelli, L., Wrigley. H., Yoon. K., Seburn, M. and Cronen, S. (2003). *What Works Study for Adult ESL Literacy Students.* Washington, DC: US Department of Education.

Cumming, J. and Gal, I., (2000). Assessment in adult numeracy education: Issues and principles for good practice. In Gal, I. (ed.) *Adult Numeracy Development: Theory, research, practice.* Cresskill, NJ: Hampton Press**:** 305–333.

DfEE (1999). *A Fresh Start: Improving literacy and numeracy. The report of the Working Group chaired by Sir Claus Moser.* London: Department for Education and Employment (DfEE).

DfEE (2001). *Skills for Life: The national strategy for improving adult literacy and numeracy skills.* London: Department for Education and Employment (UK).

DfES (2001). *Adult Numeracy Core Curriculum.* London: Department for Education and Skills (DfES).

DfES (2003a). *Skills for Life. The national strategy for improving literacy and numeracy skills – Focus on delivery to 2007.* London: Department for Education and Skills.

DfES (2003b). *The Skills for Life Survey: A national needs and impact survey of literacy, numeracy and ICT skills.* London: Department for Education and Skills.

DfES. (2005a). Numeracy Framework. Retrieved 5 January, 2006, from http://www.standards.dfes.gov.uk/numeracy/teaching_resources/.

DfES (2005b). *14–19 Education and Skills.* Norwich: The Stationery Office.

DfES/DWP/HMT (2005). *Skills: Getting On in Business, Getting On at Work.* Norwich: The Stationery Office.

DfES/FENTO (2002). *Subject Specifications for Teachers of Adult Literacy and Numeracy.* London: Department for Education and Skills.

Dowling, P. (1991). The contextualizing of mathematics: Towards a theoretical map. In Harris, M. (ed.) *Schools, Mathematics and Work.* Basingstoke: Falmer Press**:** 93–120.

Dowling, P. (1998). *Sociology of Mathematics Education: Mathematical myths/pedagogic texts.* London: Falmer Press.

Ecclestone, K. (2003). *Understanding Assessment and Qualifications in Post-Compulsory Education: Principles, politics and practice.* Leicester: National Institute of Adult Continuing Education (NIACE).

Galton, M. (1989). *Teaching in the Primary School.* London: Fulton.

Hammer, D. (1997). Discovery learning and discovery teaching. *Cognition and Instruction* **15**(4): 485–529.

House of Commons Committee of Public Accounts. (2005). *Skills for Life: Improving adult literacy and numeracy*. Report, together with formal minutes, oral and written evidence. (No. HC 792). London: The Stationery Office Limited.

Ivanič, R. and Tseng, M.-i. L. (2005). *Understanding the Relationships between Learning and Teaching: An analysis of the contribution of applied linguistics*. London: National Research and Development Centre for Adult Literacy and Numeracy (NRDC).

Kelly, S., Soundranayagam, L., and Grief, S. (2004). *Teaching and Learning Writing: A review of research and practice*. London: National Research and Development Centre for Adult Literacy and Numeracy (NRDC).

Kruidenier, J. (2002). *Research-based Principles for Adult Basic Education Reading Instruction*. Washington, DC: National Institute for Literacy & the Partnership for Reading.

Kyambi, S. (2005). *Beyond Black and White: Mapping New Immigrant Communities*. London: IPPR.

Lave, J. (1988). *Cognition in Practice: Mind, mathematics and culture in everyday life*. Cambridge: Cambridge University Press.

Learning and Skills Council (2005). *Learning and Skills – the agenda for change – the prospectus*. Learning and Skills Council.

Leitch, S. (2005). *Skills in the UK: The long-term challenge*. Interim Report. London: HM Treasury.

Lucas, N., Casey, H., Loo, S., McDonald, J. and Giannakaki, M. (2004). *New Initial Teacher Education Programmes for Teachers of Literacy, Numeracy and ESOL 2002/03: An exploratory study*. London: National Research and Development Centre for Adult Literacy and Numeracy (NRDC).

Ma, L. (1999). *Knowing and Teaching Elementary Mathematics: Teachers' understanding of fundamental mathematics in China and the United States*. Mahwah, NJ: Lawrence Erlbaum Associates.

Machin, S., McIntosh, S., Vignoles, A., and Viitanen, T. (2001). *Basic Skills, Soft Skills and Labour Market Outcomes: Secondary analysis of the National Child Development Study*. London: DfEE Research Centre for the Economics of Education, London School of Economics.

Mellar, H., Kambouri, M., Sanderson, M., and Pavlou, V. (2004). *ICT and Adult Literacy, Numeracy and ESOL*. London: National Research and Development Centre for Adult Literacy and Numeracy (NRDC).

Mortimore, P., Sammons, P., Stoll, L., Lewis, D. and Ecob, R. (1988) *School Matters: The Junior Years*. Wells: Open Books.

NRDC (2003). *Strategy: 2003–2007. Generating knowledge and transforming it into practice*. London, National Research and Development Centre for Adult Literacy and Numeracy (NRDC).

Parsons, S. and Bynner, J. (2005). *Does Numeracy Matter More?* London: National Research and Development Centre for Adult Literacy and Numeracy (NRDC).

Parsons, S., Bynner, J. and Foudouli, V. (2005). Measuring basic skills for longitudinal study. The design and development of instruments for use with cohort members in the age 34 follow-up in the 1970 British Cohort Study (BCS70). London, National Research and Development Centre for Adult Literacy and Numeracy (NRDC). From http://www.nrdc.org.uk/content.asp?CategoryID=424

QCA (2000). *National Standards for Adult Literacy and Numeracy*. London: Qualifications and Curriculum Authority (QCA).

QCA (2005). *Functional Skills Update*. London: Qualifications and Curriculum Authority.

Rampton, B. (1990). Displacing the 'native speaker': Expertise, affiliation and inheritance. *ELT Journal* 44–2: 97–101

Roberts, C., Baynham, M., Shrubshall, P., Barton, D., Chopra, P., Cooke, M., Hodge, R., Pitt, K., Schellekens, P., Wallace, C. and Whitfield, S. (2004). *English for Speakers of Other Languages (ESOL) – Case studies of provision, learners' needs and resources*. London: National Research and Development Centre for Adult Literacy and Numeracy.

Schuller, T., Brassett-Grundy, A., Green, A., Hammond, C. and Preston, J. (2002). *Learning, Continuity and Change in Adult Life*. London: Institute of Education/The Centre for Research on the Wider Benefits of Learning.

Smith, A. (2004). *Making Mathematics Count: The Report of Professor Adrian Smith's Inquiry into Post-14 Mathematics Education*. London: The Stationery Office.

Swain, J., Baker, E., Holden, D., Newmarch, B. and Coben, D. (2005). *'Beyond the Daily Application': Making numeracy teaching meaningful to adult learners*. London: National Research and Development Centre for Adult Literacy and Numeracy (NRDC).

Tomlinson, M. (2004). *14–19 Curriculum and Qualifications Reform*. Final Report of the Working Group on 14–19 Reform. Annesley: Department for Education and Skills.

Torgerson, C., Brooks, G., Porthouse, J., Burton, M., Robinson, A., Wright, K. and Watt, I. (2003). *Adult literacy and numeracy interventions and outcomes: A review of controlled trials*. London: National Research and Development Centre for Adult Literacy and Numeracy (NRDC).

Torgerson, C., Brooks, G., Porthouse, J., Burton, M., Wright, K. and Watt, I. (2004) *Adult literacy and numeracy interventions and outcomes: a review of controlled trials*. London: National Research and Development Centre for Adult Literacy and Numeracy (NRDC).

Torgerson, C. J., Porthouse, J. et al. (2005). A systematic review and meta-analysis of controlled trials evaluating interventions in adult literacy and numeracy. *Journal of Research in Reading* **27**(2): 87–107.

Vygotsky, L. S. (1993). Extracts from Thought and Language and Mind in Society. In Stierer, B.

and Maybin, J. *Language, Literacy and Learning in Educational Practice*. Cleveland: Multilingual Matters.

White, A (2002). *Social Focus in Brief: Ethnicity 2002.* Norwich: National Statistics.

Winter, R. (1992). Mathophobia, Pythagoras and roller-skating. In Nickson, M. and Lerman, S. (eds) *The Social Context of Mathematics Education: Theory and practice*. London: South Bank Press: 81–93.

Wood, D., Bruner, J. S. et al. (1976). The role of tutoring in problem solving *Journal of Child Psychology and Psychiatry* **17**(2): 89–100

Appendices

Appendix A: Contact details of the research team

Name	Title	E-mail address
Prof. Diana Coben	Principal investigator	diana.coben@kcl.ac.uk
Prof. Margaret Brown	Principal investigator	margaret.brown@kcl.ac.uk
Dr Valerie Rhodes	Researcher	valerie.rhodes@kcl.ac.uk
Dr Jon Swain	Researcher	J.Swain@ioe.ac.uk
Dr Katerina Ananiadou	Researcher	kat_ananiadou@yahoo.co.uk

Appendix B: A note on ethnicity, nationality and language

Some of these categories concerning learners' background characteristics proved to be more problematic than others: in particular, those of ethnicity and first language. Learners come from many different ethnic, national and linguistic backgrounds, and for pedagogic and equal opportunity reasons, one or more of these is recorded, depending on their usefulness for the particular project. However, available categories do not necessarily fit with people's own sense of identity. Ethnicity and nationality are highly problematic, contested, and historically variable concepts. Ethnicity, in particular, is constructed out of overlapping categories based on colour, nationality, religion, culture and language. People often move strategically between ethnicities by using bilingualism, dual nationality, multiple identities and repertoires of cultural knowledge (White, 2002: 4). A fixed category can stereotype and give ethnicity or nationality an emphasis over and above other social categories that people belong to. In addition, most monitoring systems do not reflect the changes in immigration patterns which have led to 'hyper-diversity' (Kyambi, 2005) in the London region and, increasingly, elsewhere. The 'other' category for those not from the settled communities now includes people from the Middle East, Asia (outside the Indian sub-continent), South America and the Accession states of the new Europe, as well as many other smaller groupings.

Recording language background is also notoriously difficult as there is no straightforward link between ethnic category, nationality, ethnic identity and language. Learners' stated language backgrounds are often a mix of languages they are expert in, languages they have an attachment to and ones which are part of their inheritance (Rampton, 1990). And they may use varieties of these languages, and only their written or spoken forms. However, ethnic/national/language monitoring is an important tool in tackling social exclusion and understanding teaching and learning. So, the project used six categories for identifying these aspects of learner background, while acknowledging their limitations.

Glossary of statistical terms

Analysis of Variance (ANOVA): statistical technique that aims to compare the means of two or more groups of one or more independent variables on one dependent variable in order to ascertain if the group means are significantly different from each other.

Causation: the concept that variation in one variable causes variation in another variable.

Chi square: a statistic used to compare observed and expected frequencies in sample data. Observed frequencies are the actual (or observed) number of cases in the cells, rows or columns of a contingency table of two categorical (nominal) variables. Expected frequencies are the number of cases that one would expect to appear in a cell, row totals or column totals based on probability alone.

Correlation coefficient: a statistic that reveals the strength and direction of the relationship between two variables. Correlation co-efficients can range from −1.00 (indicating a perfect negative correlation) to +1.00 (indicating a perfect positive correlation). A correlation co-efficient of 0 indicates that there is no relationship between the variables being examined.

Curvilinear relationship: a relationship between two variables that is positive at some values but negative at other values.

Dependent or outcome variable: A variable for which the values may depend on the value of the independent variable. When it is statistically related to the independent variable, the value of the dependent variable 'depends on', or is predicted by, the value of the independent variable.

Effect size (*d*): A measure of the size of the effect observed in some statistic. It is a way of determining the practical (rather than statistical) significance of a statistic by reducing the impact of sample size. The closer the value of *d* is to 1, the larger the effect size of the statistic.

***F* statistic (or ratio)**: the statistic produced by ANOVA and used to indicate the average amount of difference between group means relative to the average amount of variance within each group.

Factor analysis: a statistical technique used to simplify complex sets of data by reducing a large number of variables to a smaller number of *factors*, i.e. constructs or dimensions which can account for the relationships (correlations) between the variables.

Independent or predictor variable: A variable that may predict or produce variation in the dependent variable.

Multiple regression: Statistical technique that allows researchers to make predictions about the value of a dependent variable given certain values in a group of independent or predictor variables. The analysis provides information on how much the group of predictor variables is related to the dependent variable, the strength of the relationship between each predictor variable and the dependent variable *while controlling for the other predictor variables in the* *model* and the relative strength of each predictor variable.

Pearson product-moment correlation coefficient: a statistic indicating the strength and direction of a correlation between two continuous variables, i.e. variables measured with numerical values with equal distance between each number.

Positive/negative correlation: a positive correlation between two variables indicates that as scores on one variable increase, scores on the other variable also increase, and vice versa. In contrast, a negative correlation indicates that as scores on one variable increase, scores on the other variable decrease, and vice versa.

R **square**: the percentage of variance in the dependent variable explained by the regression model.

Reliability coefficient (Cronbach's alpha): a measure indicating the internal consistency, or reliability, of a multiple item scale. Alpha is based on the average correlation of each item in the scale with every other item. It can range from 0 (indicating very low internal consistency) to 1 (indicating perfect internal consistency).

Spearman rho coefficient: the correlation coefficient used to measure the association between two ordinal scale variables, i.e. numerical variables where the numbers are meaningful but the distance between them is not constant, such as ranked data.

Standard deviation: the average deviation between the individual scores in a distribution and the mean of the distribution.

Statistical significance (*p* value): this is a probability level (ranging from 0 to 1) that indicates the likelihood that a particular result could have arisen by chance. In the social sciences, a statistic with an associated *p* value of 0.05 or less is generally considered 'significant'; this means that the probability that this result was due to chance or random variation is 5 per cent or less.

t **test**: a statistical test used to compare the means between two groups to find out if they are significantly different from each other.